Art Assessments

Tests, Quizzes, Benchmarks, Exams, Rubrics, and More for Art Teachers

by Eric Gibbons
Copyright 2013

ISBN-13:978-1-940290-04-1
ISBN-10:194029004X

Printed Name of purchaser: _____

Signature of purchaser: _____

Date of Purchase: ___/___/_____

Venue of purchase _____

Contents:

The sequence this book follows:

Quarter 1: Art Elements and Color

Quarter 2: Art Principles and Color

Quarter 3: Art History and Critique

Quarter 4: Integration of the above

Dear Colleague,

In perfect world with administrators that understand the importance of art, and an education system that wasn't addicted to the false notion that testing reveals knowledge, formal "testing" might be unnecessary. Assessing progress in concrete ways is what more and more districts are required to do. I hope this book offers some possibilities based in "reality," from a teacher who has actually used them, as opposed to a state official with no idea what an art room even looks like.

We know art may be the most important class a student will ever take. When we grid, measure, and use perspective—we learn about geometry. When we make sculptures—we learn engineering. When we mix colors—we reveal information about physics. When we write about our work—we reinforce these skills. When we create illustrations for stories—we learn about literature. When we review the styles of art from da Vinci to Warhol—we understand more about history. Art is the meeting place for all subjects.

According to The College Board and Americans for the Arts, students who have four years of art score, on average, 91 points higher on their *SATs. My own experience shows that my students are 50% more likely to pass the HSPA exam in their junior year when they have taken my class. These are numbers that administrators care about.

Enclosed in this book are all of my exams, quizzes, tests, benchmarks, and written assignments that I have developed over that last quarter century in my classroom. You are welcome to photo copy these pages for your students, or use the ideas I have included and augment them for your own program. You may handle the material differently. I am aware that some programs define principles and elements with slight differences, but this program has worked well for me.

If the few "Scantron" (*test forms with A,B,C,D,E, bubble answers*) format tests look a bit odd, you'll find, statistically, they work. They offer students a 20% curve on the exams should they guess, just like many other traditional assessments. I have included both the Scantron versions and the "write-in" versions for you to choose from. Some students have an IEP/504 that precludes them from using certain testing formats.

Should you have any questions, comments, corrections, etc, feel free to contact me via the Firehouse Publications website at www.FirehousePublications.com. Be sure to include a clear subject so you get a fast reply. You will find many excellent resources there for art teachers, particularly "The Art Student's Workbook." The teacher's edition includes nearly 3 years of both 2D and 3D lessons, and a whole lot more.

Thank you,
Eric Gibbons

* http://tinyurl.com/mo2uzpb

The 8 Art Elements

A line is the most simple thing in art. We call it an art element. You need lines to draw anything. What can you measure about a line? _____
What are some lines you see around you?

Draw 3 different kinds of lines here:

1	2	3

A line that touches itself makes a shape. A shape is ____ -D because we can measure the _____ and _____ of it. "D" is short for Dimension. There are #____ basic shapes. Draw the basic shapes below:

_____ put together can create a form. A box is a form made from 6 square shapes. In art we call a box a special name. Think of the ice in your freezer at home. You don't call them *ice boxes*, you call them ice _____. You eat ice cream in a _____, that's another basic form. What are the other two basic forms? _____ and _____.
Can you draw all the forms below?

Color is sometimes the first thing we see. Most colors we see are mixed from just #_____ basic colors. These colors are _____, _____, _____. The other name for basic colors is _____ colors. When basic colors mix, they make new colors. We call them _____ colors. Try mixing the basic colors below to see what colors they make. (Use marker, crayon, or color pencil)

Red and blue	Red and yellow	Yellow and blue

All things, art and not-art, take up _____. It comes in two kinds, _____ where the thing is, and _____ which is the empty area around it. When you swim in a pool, you are in the _____ _____ of the water. When you are in school, you are in the _____ _____ of the building.

Everything around us we can see has weight. Even air has weight! What is another word for weight? _____ . Sometimes things look heavier or lighter than they really are. Metal and rocks are things we think of when we see dark colors. Cotton and clouds are things we think of when we see light colors. _____ colors often look heavier than _____ colors.

Everything you touch has a feeling; smooth, rough, wet, dry, etc. This is the art element of _____ .

Draw 3 examples below:

1	2	3

The last art element might be the most important. Without it we cannot even see any of the rest. What can it be? _____ . When we draw, we sometimes add shadows, which are the opposite of this art element.

Review Pages: The 8 Art Elements

A line is the most simple thing in art. We call it an art element. You need lines to draw anything. What can you measure about a line? __length or how long it is__
What are some lines you see around you?

- *Table edges, edges of bricks, lines on paper, etc...*

Draw 3 different kinds of lines here: *Any line is okay __if it is not a closed shape__*

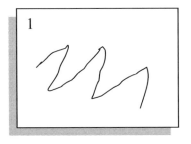 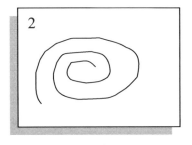 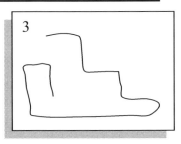

A line that touches itself makes a shape. A shape is __2__ -D because we can measure the __length__ and __width__ of it. "D" is short for Dimension. There are #__3__ basic shapes. Draw the basic shapes below:

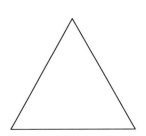 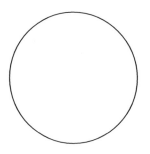 

__Shapes__ put together can create a form. A box is a form made from 6 square shapes. In art we call a box a special name. Think of the ice in your freezer at home. You don't call them *ice boxes*, you call them ice __cubes__. You eat ice cream in a __cone__, that's another basic form. What are the other two basic forms? __cylinder__ and __sphere__.

Can you draw all the forms below?

Color is sometimes the first thing we see. Most colors we see are mixed from just # **3** basic colors. These colors are **red** , **yellow** , **blue** . The other name for basic colors is **primary** colors. When basic colors mix, they make new colors. We call them **secondary** colors. Try mixing the basic colors below to see what colors they make. (Use marker, crayon, or color pencil)

Red and blue **PURPLE**	Red and yellow **ORANGE**	Yellow and blue **GREEN**

All things, art and not-art, take up **space** . It comes in two kinds, **positive** where the thing is, and **negative** which is the empty area around it. When you swim in a pool, you are in the **positive** space of the water. When you are in school, you are in the **negative** space of the building.

Everything around us we can see has weight. Even air has weight! What is another word for weight? **mass** . Sometimes things look heavier or lighter than they really are. Metal and rocks are things we think of when we see dark colors. Cotton and clouds are things we think of when we see light colors. **dark** colors often look heavier than **light** colors.

Everything you touch has a feeling; smooth, rough, wet, dry, etc. This is the art element of **texture** .

Draw 3 examples below: *(Any 3 different textures would be fine)*

1	2	3
ROUGH Texture	**SMOOTH Texture**	**WOOD Texture**

The last art element might be the most important. Without it we cannot even see any of the rest. What can it be? **light** . When we draw, we sometimes add shadows, which are the opposite of this art element.

Overview of 8 Art Elements

A line is a _____ moving through _____. We can measure the _____ of a line and nothing else, therefore it is _____ dimensional or ____ -D.

A _____ that intersects itself will create a shape. A shape is _____ dimensional. There are _____ basic shapes. The one with the fewest number of sides is the _____. The one with the most sides is the _____.

A _____ that moves in _____ can create a form. There are ____ basic forms. The one with the fewest amount of sides is the _____, the one with the most sides is the _____.

There are ____ basic colors. Basic colors are also called _____ colors. When these basic colors mix they create _____ colors of which there are ____. Color is _____ light. Orange, red and yellow are considered _____ colors, while blue, green, and purple are considered _____ colors.

_____ refers to the weight of something; sometimes it is real and sometimes it is the way it looks. A _____ colored box will look heavier than a _____ colored one.

The roughness or smoothness of a surface refers to its _____. It can sometimes be made by repeating an art _____ many times.

All objects, art and non-art, take up _____. Many art elements move through it. This art element comes in 2 types, they are _____ meaning where the object IS, and _____, meaning where the object is NOT.

The art element of _____ helps us see all other art elements. We see everything because it is _____ off of an object or surface and back to our eye. When it is NOT bounced back to us we see _____.

8 Art Elements Review
Remember that principles **organize** the Elements

A **line** is a point moving through space. We can measure the length of a line and nothing else about it; therefore it is one-dimensional or 1-D.

A line that intersects itself will create a **shape**. A shape is 2-dimensional. There are 3 basic shapes. They are the triangle, circle, and square.

A shape that moves in space can create a **form**. There are 4 basic forms. They are the cylinder, cone, cube, and sphere.

There are 3 basic **colors**. Basic colors are also called primary colors. When these basic colors mix they create secondary colors of which there are 3. Color is reflected light. Orange, red, and yellow are considered warm colors, while blue, green, and purple are considered cool colors.

 KNOW the color wheel and mixtures.

Complementary = opposite, analogous = neighboring.

Mass refers to the weight of something, sometimes it is real and sometimes it is the way it looks. A dark colored box will look heavier than a light colored one.

The roughness or smoothness of a surface refers to its **texture**. It can sometimes be made by repeating an art element many times. For example if you draw 100 lines, they will no longer be seen as lines, but as a texture; like grass.

All objects, art and non-art, take up **space**. Many art elements move through it. This art element comes in 2 types; Positive Space, meaning where the object IS, and Negative Space, meaning where the object is NOT.

The art element of **light** helps us see all other art elements. We see everything because it is reflected off an object or surface and back to our eyes. When it is NOT bounced back to us, we see black, or nothing.

A	1
B	2
C	3
D	4
E	Balance
A	black
B	brown
C	circle
D	color
E	cone
A	cool
B	cube
C	cylinder
A	dark
E	Depth
C	element
D	form
E	Length
C	light
B	line
C	mass
D	negative
E	neutral
B	Point
C	positive
D	primary
E	rectangle
A	reflected
B	secondary
A	Shadow
B	shape
E	Space
A	sphere
B	square
D	texture
E	triangle
B	warm
C	white
D	Width

Elements Test   NAME_____pd__

WARNING! Some answers are used MORE than once, <u>some are never used.</u> Use the letter in front of the correct word for your Scantron sheet. If 2 answers are correct, they should have the same letter in front. The "#" means the answer is a number.

A line is a _1_____ moving through _2_____. We can measure the _3____ of a line and nothing else; therefore it is _#4_____ dimensional or _#5_____ -D.

A _6_____ that intersects itself will create a shape. A Shape is _#7_____ dimensional. There are _#8_____ basic shapes. The one with the fewest amounts of sides is the __9_____ the one with the most sides is the _10_____.

A _11_____ that moves in _12_____ can create a form. There are _#13_____ basic forms. The one with the fewest amounts of sides is the __14_____ the one with the most sides is the _15_____.

There are _#16_____ basic colors. Basic colors are also called _17____ colors. When these basic colors mix they create _18_____ colors of which there are _#19_____. Color is ___20__ light. Orange, Red and Yellow are considered _21_____ colors, while Blue, Green and Purple are considered _22_____ colors.

__23_____ Refers to the weight of something, sometimes it is real and sometimes it is the way it looks. A __24_____ colored box will look heavier than a __25_____ colored one.

The roughness or smoothness of a surface refers to its _26_____. It can sometimes be made by repeating an art _27_____ many times.

All objects, art and non-art, take up _28_____. Many art elements move through it. This art element comes in 2 types, they are _29_____ meaning where the object IS, and __30_____, meaning where the object is NOT.

The art element of _31_____ helps us see all other art elements. We see everything because it is _32_____ off of an object or surface and back to our eye. When it is NOT bounced back to us we see _33_____.

Please see the teacher's example artwork. The artist is _____
The name of the artwork is _____ dated _____
          Please write a paragraph on the back of your scantron on how each art element is present or not within the artwork. Please be specific so it is obvious that you know what the art elements are.

1
2
3
4
Balance
black
brown
circle
color
cone
cool
cube
cylinder
dark
Depth
element
form
Length
light
line
mass
negative
neutral
Point
positive
primary
rectangle
reflected
secondary
Shadow
shape
Space
sphere
square
texture
triangle
warm
white
Width

Elements Test   NAME_____pd__

WARNING! Some answers are used MORE than once, <u>some are never used.</u> Write your answer on the blank line. The "#" means the answer is a number.

A line is a _____ moving through _____. We can measure the _____ of a line and nothing else, therefore it is _#_____ dimensional or _#_____ -D.

A _____ That intersects itself will create a shape. A Shape is _#_____ dimensional. There are _#_____ basic shapes. The one with the fewest amount of sides is the _____ the one with the most sides is the _____.

A _____ that moves in _____ can create a form. There are _#_____ basic forms. The one with the fewest amount of sides is the _____ the one with the most sides is the _____.

There are _#_____ basic colors. Basic colors are also called _____ colors. When these basic colors mix they create _____ colors of which there are _#_____. Color is _____ light. Orange, Red and Yellow are considered _____ colors, while Blue, Green and Purple are considered _____ colors.

_____ Refers to the weight of something, sometimes it is real and sometimes it is the way it looks. A _____ colored box will look heavier than a _____ colored one.

The roughness or smoothness of a surface refers to it's _____. It can sometimes be made by repeating an art _____ many times.

All objects, art and non-art, take up _____. Many art elements move through it. This art element comes in 2 types, they are _____ meaning where the object IS, and _____, meaning where the object is NOT.

The art element of _____ Helps us see all other art elements. We see everything because it is _____ off of an object or surface and back to our eye. When it is NOT bounced back to us we see _____.

Please see the teacher's example artwork. The artist is _____
The name of the artwork is _____ dated _____
    Please write a paragraph on the back of this paper on how each art element is present or not within the artwork. Please be specific so it is obvious that you know what the art elements are.

Principles of Art & Design

1. What does **balance** mean?

2. Draw two things balanced below:

3. Can you draw one thing balanced by many smaller ones below?

4. Try drawing something that is moving. How do you make it look like its moving? **Movement** is an art principal.

5. What is **contrast**? _____

Can you draw two opposite objects below?

6. What is **unity**? _____

Can you draw some things in unity below?

7. What is **emphasis**? (*em-fa-sis*) _____

8. Draw sometime below and make one thing stand out with emphasis.

9. What is **pattern**? _____

Please draw 3 patterns below.

| 1 | 2 | 3 |

10. Draw two kinds of patterns below: a planned pattern and an organic pattern.

Planned/Mechanical   Organic/Natural

| 1 | 2 |

11. What is **variety**?

12. How is variety different from **contrast**?

13. Do a drawing of your shoe on the next page. Label three or more of the art principals you can see in your drawing.

SHOE SKETCH

Name_____ Pd.___

Art Principles Worksheet   (tiny sketch below)

The artwork sample is called:

_____

by _____.

_____ is the style of art.

Where do you see unity?

Where do you see variety?

Where do you see contrast or opposites?

What is emphasized in the art? What is the main important part?

Where do you see movement?

How does the artist balance the picture?

What kinds of patterns can you see?

TEACHER: Put up a poster from art history and have students complete this form

Art Principles Worksheet

(tiny sketch below)

The artwork sample is called:

_____

by _____.

_____ is the style of art.

Where do you see unity?

Where do you see variety?

Where do you see contrast or opposites?

What is emphasized in the art? What is the main important part?

Where do you see movement?

How does the artist balance the picture?

What kinds of patterns can you see?

Principles of Art & Design -Answers-

1. What does **balance** mean?
   - Two things of equal weight

2. Draw two things balanced below:

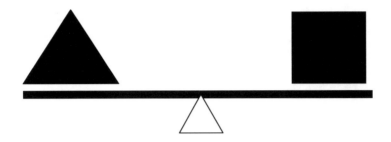

3. Can you draw one thing balanced by many smaller ones below?

Something like this is fine

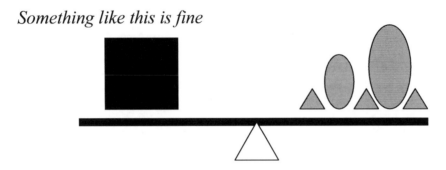

4. Try drawing something that is moving. How do you make it look like its moving? **Movement** is an art principal.

Swish lines are okay, or something in the act of moving.

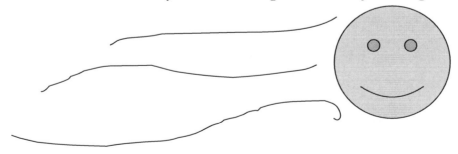

5. What is **contrast**? ___opposites like light and dark, or big and small...___
Can you draw two opposite objects below?

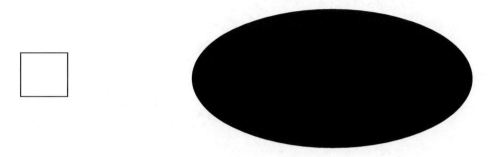

6. What is **unity**? ___having something the same, like most trees are green___
Can you draw some things in unity below?

All circle shapes:

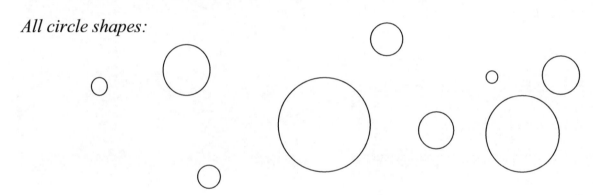

7. What is **emphasis**? (*em-fa-sis*) **something that stands out because its different**

8. Draw sometime below and make one thing stand out with emphasis.

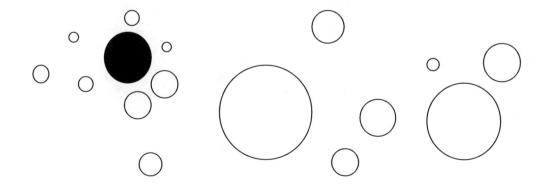

9. What is **pattern**? **A repeated shape or line, it can be planned or natural**
Please draw 3 patterns below.

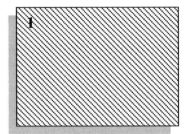 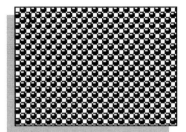 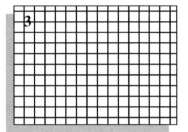

10. Draw two kinds of patterns below: a planned pattern and an organic pattern.

Planned/Mechanical   Organic/Natural

11. What is **variety**?
   - **Having many different things in a picture; people, trees, houses, cars…**

12. How is variety different from **contrast**?
   - **Contrast is just 2 things being opposite, variety is many different things.**

Let's Learn About Color

Shade is the opposite of _____. Without shadow we would all look flat like a cartoon picture. In art we draw shadows to show that things take up space. They usually have one side in light, and another side that is shaded. Sometimes people draw shadows with black or gray, but you can also use cool colors like green, purple, or blue. I drew a ball below with a shadow. You try and draw something with a shadow too.

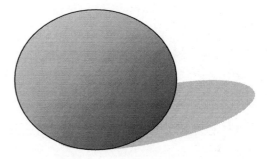

Primary Colors (Pry-mary) are sometimes called the basic colors. Primary means *first* or *the beginning*. Just like Primary school is for grades one through about six. There are #_____ primary colors. These colors are _____, _____, and _____.

When you make a cake, you need to use eggs. If you don't have eggs, can you just use pickles or jelly instead? NO, you have to go out and get some eggs. Eggs are a primary ingredient. You cannot put things together to make an egg, you have to go and get it.

This is just like the primary colors. You cannot mix a primary color, you have to go get it. This is why they are so special. Almost every color you see around you is a primary color, or was made from mixing primary colors.

Use only your primary colors, and draw your shoe or bookbag below.

Secondary Colors are like the children of the primary colors. Secondary means the second layer of color, after primaries. Just like secondary school is after primary school. When two primary colors mix, they make a secondary color. Use crayons, pastels, or colored pencils to color in the circles below with primary colors. See what colors they make when they mix.

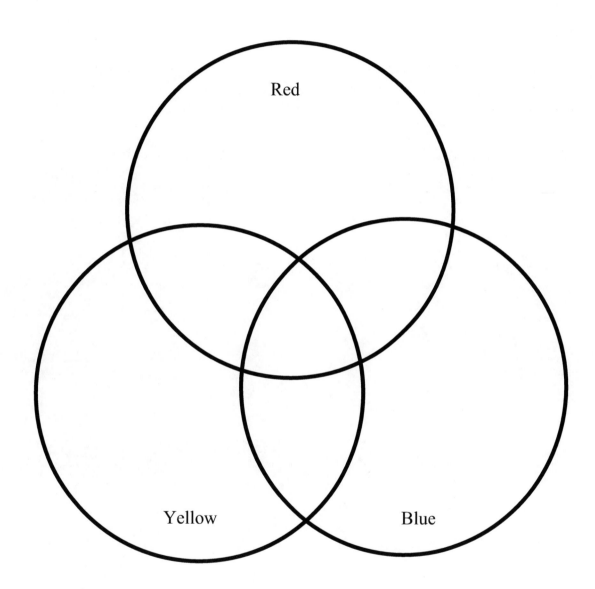

Want to know more? The color in the middle has a long and special name.

_____ _____.

Spectrum is the colors in a rainbow. A rainbow is made when the water drops in the air splits the white light from the sun into all the colors we can see in a rainbow. These colors are red, orange, yellow, green, blue, and purple. They are always in this order. These are also all the primary and secondary colors.

Please fill in the colors of the rainbow in the picture below, starting with red.

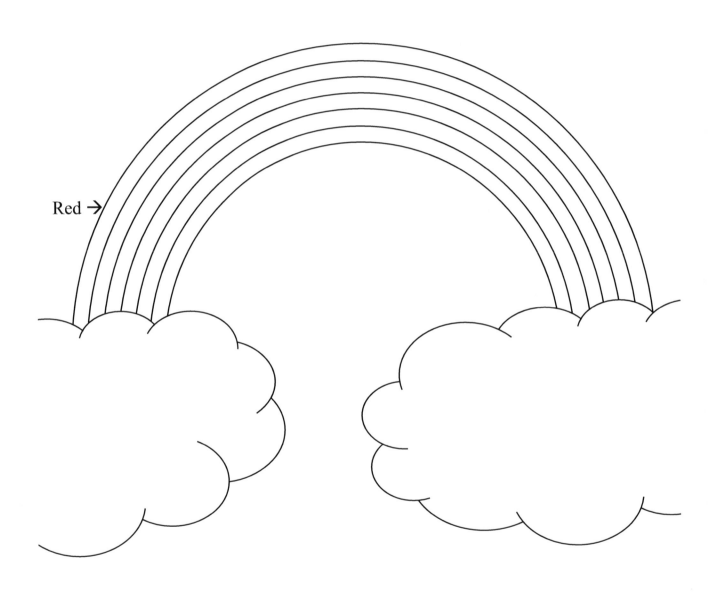

Red →

Let's Learn About Color - ANSWERS

Shade is the opposite of **light**. Without shadow we would all look flat like a magazine picture. In art we draw shadows to show that things take up space. They usually have one side in light, and another that is shaded. Sometimes people draw shadows with black or gray, but you can also use cool colors like green, purple, or blue. I drew a ball below with a shadow.

Primary Colors are sometimes called the basic colors. Primary means first or the beginning. Just like Primary school is for grades one through about six. There are **# 3** primary colors. These colors are ___**Red**___ , ___**Yellow**___ , and ___**Blue**___ .

Secondary Colors

- Orange, Green, Purple

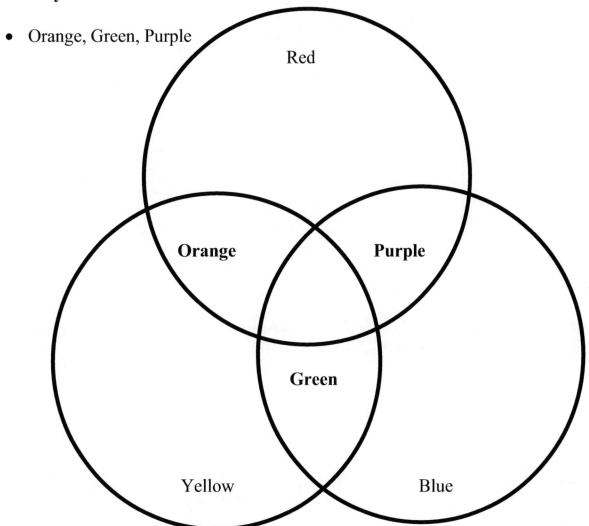

Want to know more? The color in the middle has a long and special name.

___**Chromatic**___ ___**Gray**___ .

Analogous Colors (*Ah-nail-la-gus*) These are neighboring colors. When you look at the rainbow, red is next to orange, so they are analogous colors. The only strange one is red and purple. If a rainbow was in a circle, like the color wheel below, then you can see how they are neighboring colors too.

COLOR WHEEL →

Use only the 3 primary colors to color in this color wheel →

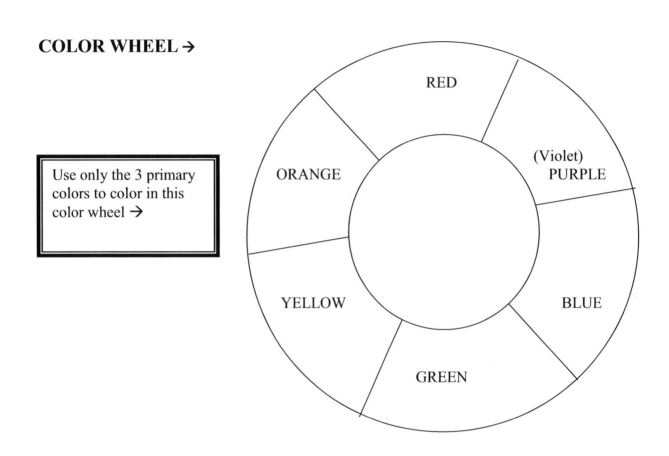

How can you remember the colors of the spectrum? We know they are red, orange, yellow, green, blue, and purple. It might help to make a silly sentence to help you remember. What sentence can you make? The first word should start with an "R" for red. Then "O" for orange, and so on. Try to make a sentence below for you to remember your spectrum.

R_____ O_____ Y_____ G_____ B_____ P_____ .

Complementary Colors: (*Com-pla-men-tary*) These are colors that are on opposite sides of the color wheel. When you look back you will see that colors like blue and orange are on opposite sides. When you mix opposites, you get a really muddy or dirty looking color. This is called Chromatic Gray. (Kro-mat-tik) If colors were perfect, the gray would look like a real gray, but it just looks like brown to us.

Complimentary colors are often used for holidays. What holiday goes with each pair of colors? Can you draw a whole holiday scene with just 2 complimentary colors?

1. Red and green are used in this holiday: _____

2. Blue and orange are used in this holiday: _____

3. Purple and Yellow are used in this holiday: _____

Mini-holiday picture below:

Monochromatic: (*ma-no-kro-ma-tic*) Mono = one, Chroma = color, so mochromatic means *of one color*. If you did a monochromatic picture in blue, you would do it in all kinds of blue; light blue, dark blue, medium blue. You could even add black or white. Many artists make colors lighter or darker by pressing harder or softer with their crayons or pencils. Can you use one color to create a picture of something below? What is your favorite color?

Warm Colors: Warm colors should remind you of warm things. Think of fire, the sun, a hot stove; what colors are these things?

_____, _____, _____.

Warm colors are active colors. They have lots of energy because they are so bright.

Draw something hot below and only use your warm colors OR draw yourself doing something very active, like a sport, and use just warm colors.

Cool Colors: cool colors should remind you of cool or cold things. Think water, the ocean, a river, grass, or the sky when it's getting dark; what colors are these?

_____, _____, _____.

Cool colors are calm colors. They are relaxing and have little energy.

Draw something peaceful below and only use your cool colors OR draw yourself doing something very relaxing, like taking a nap, relaxing with friends, or strolling through a park using only cool colors.

COLOR ANSWERS:

Complementary Colors: (*Com-pla-men-tary*) These are colors that are on opposite sides of the color wheel. When you look back you will see that colors like blue and orange are on opposite sides. When you mix opposites, you get a really muddy or dirty looking color. This is called Chromatic Gray. (Kro-mat-tik) If colors were perfect, the gray would look like a real gray, but it just looks like brown to us.

Complimentary colors are often used for holidays. What holiday goes with each pair of colors? Can you draw a whole holiday scene with just 2 complimentary colors?

1. Red and green are used in this holiday: Christmas/Winter Holidays

2. Blue and orange are used in this holiday: Halloween

3. Purple and Yellow are used in this holiday: Easter/Spring Holiday

_____

Warm Colors: Warm colors should remind you of warm things. Think of fire, the sun, a hot stove; what colors are these things?

 Red , **Orange** , **Yellow**

_____

Cool Colors: cool colors should remind you of cool or cold things. Think water, the ocean, a river, grass, or the sky when it's getting dark; what colors are these?

 Blue , **Purple** , **Green** .

Coloring Practice:

Start with shape number 1. Color it in neatly; try to stay in the lines. When you are done, show it to your teacher. They will tell you how you did, and what you can do to make it better. Then you can do the next one. Show your teacher after you finish each shape. This is a chance to show off your coloring skills.

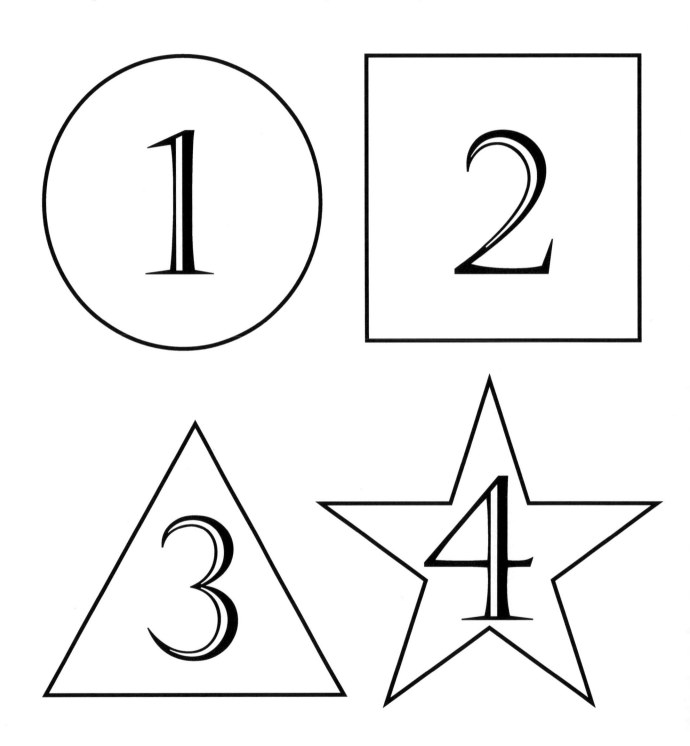

Colors and Shapes have feelings too!

Red is the color of blood, stop signs, and lava. How do these things make you feel?

Orange is the color of a hot stove burner, warning signs, and some spicy sauces. How do these things make people feel?

Yellow is the color of the sun, smiley faces, and many flowers. How do these things make people feel?

Green is the color of grass, healthy vegetables, and many things that grow. What feelings does this give people?

Blue is the color of the ocean and the sky. When you are relaxing at the beach or laying down looking up at the sky on a beautiful day, how do you feel?

Purple is the color of royalty, deep oceans, and starry nights. What kinds of feelings do these give you?

Triangles are sharp like broken glass, knives, and arrows. How would you feel if these were on the ground all around you?

Circles are soft like balloons, balls, bubbles, and hoopla-hoops. How do these things make you feel?

Squares are used to make bricks, boxes, buildings, and tables. Why do we not use circles to make bricks, boxes, and buildings? (*Because squares and boxes are…*)

Now that we see that colors and shapes can represent feelings, what shapes would you be most like? Are you mostly a square because you are strong, or would you say you are more playful like a circle? Can you be both? We can mix shapes together to make new shapes. If you have a bit of a temper, but most of the time you are a serious person, what shapes would you put together? _____ and _____ . Would that look like a house shape?

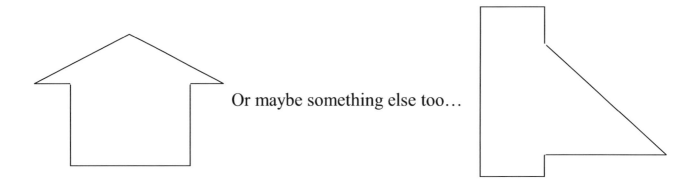

Or maybe something else too…

On the next page, draw a shape that is a mix of shapes as a symbol for you. Use colors and patterns too that help show your personality.

Draw a shape that is a mix of shapes as a symbol for you. Use colors and patterns too that help show your personality below.

Colors and Shapes have feelings too! - Answers

Red is the color of blood, stop signs, and lava. How do these things make you feel?
- **Scared, troubled, danger, fear...**

Orange is the color of a hot stove burner, warning signs, and some spicy sauces. How do these things make people feel?
- **Worried, anxious, nervous, excited, full of energy...**

Yellow is the color of the sun, smiley faces, and many flowers. How do these things make people feel?
- **Cheerful, joyful, energy, warm...**

Green is the color of grass, healthy vegetables, and many things that grow. What feelings does this give people?
- **Growing, happy, pleasant, smart, healthy...**

Blue is the color of the ocean and the sky. When you are relaxing at the beach or laying down looking up at the sky on a beautiful day, how do you feel?
- **Nice, calm, quiet, restful...**

Purple is the color of royalty, deep oceans, and starry nights. What kinds of feelings does this give people?
- **Sleep, silence, cold, alone...**

Triangles are sharp like broken glass, knives, and arrows. How would you feel if you were surrounded by these things?
- **Scared, troubled, danger, fear...**

Circles are soft like balloons, balls, bubbles, and hoopla-hoops. How do these things make people feel?
- **Cheerful, joyful, energy, playful, child-like...**

Squares are used to make bricks, boxes, buildings, and tables. We do not use circles to make bricks, boxes, and buildings because squares are more... What?
- **Sturdy, strong, dependable, boring, useful...**

Resources: "The Emotional Color Wheel" www.firehousepublications.com
Video Presentation on topic: http://tinyurl.com/c8cbevu

Art and MATH?!?

1. In every state, you need to pay sales tax on a sale, but this is added on after the purchase. What is the sales tax in your state? _____ % . So you sell your last project for $100.00, how much is the tax?

2. From questions #1, what is the price the customer has to pay for your artwork?

$_____ Show your work below:

3. Most New York galleries will keep 50% of the sale price from the art they sell. This is called a commission. So if you want $100.00 for your artwork, and the gallery will take 50%, what is the final* price of the art?
(*This is called the retail price)

$_____ Show your work below:

4. There are some grids in this workbook. How can you know the number of squares without counting each and every square? Write out how to find the answer.

_____

_____

5. There are three grids in this book. How many squares are in each?

A (big squares) _____, B (medium squares) _____, C (little squares) _____ .

Show your work here:

6. If you have a drawing that is 10 x 8 inches, and you frame it with a wood that is 3 inches wide, how large will the whole thing be with the frame?

_____ x _____ inches.

Show work here:

7. If you have a present to wrap and the box is a cube with 6 inches on each side. How many square inches of wrapping do you need to cover the whole box without wasting any paper?

_____

Show work here:

8. If you need exact measurements, why should you never measure from the end of a ruler?

_____

_____

9. Let us say your class is going to paint some art on one wall of your classroom, and it will be so large it will take up the whole wall. One gallon of paint will cover 300 square feet of wall. How many gallons of paint do you need to buy?

_____ gallons.

Show work here:

10. A gallon of paint may cost $15.00 each. So how much is the paint for your mural in number 9.

$_____.

Show work here:

11. Putting questions #9 and #10 together, how much money does your class have to get to buy all the paint for your mural in questions #9? (From #1 use the tax rate of your state, and figure out how much the price will be for 1 gallon with tax)

$_____

Show work here:

12. Look back at question #3. If you did the math right, you will have earned $100.00 for the sale of your artwork. Does this mean you have a profit of $100.00?

YES _____ / NO _____

Write why you said yes or no:

13. Question #3 says that a New York art gallery will keep 50% of the money from your art that sells. This is a lot of money. Why would a gallery take 50%?
(Do not say, "they want money," what is the *reason* why they need 50%?)

_____

_____

_____

_____

14. If your art room was an art gallery and the monthly rent is $5 per square foot, how much is it to rent the room?

How wide and long is the room? _____ x _____ feet.

Square footage of room is _____ feet squared.

The rent is $_____

Show work here:

15. If it takes 30 seconds for each student to wash his brush in a sink, (one at a time) how many minutes need to be allowed for clean-up in the classroom?

_____ minutes.

Show work here:

16. If your friend gave you a picture from a magazine that measured 8 x 10 inches, and they wanted you to do a drawing of it that was 50% bigger, how big would the paper for your drawing have to be?

_____ x _____ inches.

Show your work here:

Some Art/Math Answers

1. If your sales tax is 7% then multiply $100 by .07 and the sales tax is $7.
2. Add the above to $100. In this example the amount would be $107.00
3. Retail price is $200. 50% of $200 is $100.
4. Multiply the number of squares in the length by those in the width
5. 70, 70, 166
6. 16 x 14 inches (Remember you have frame on both sides, not one)
7. 216 in^2
8. The ends of rulers are often worn or chipped
9. Multiply the length and height of the wall and divide by 300.
10. Multiply the answer from number 9 by $15.00.
11. Multiply the answer from 10 by your sales tax amount, and add them together.
12. NO: You have to buy the paint, the paper or canvas, the frame, drive the work to the gallery, and all this costs money. Profit is the total money you earned, so you have to subtract (take away) the money it costs to make the art.
13. Rent in New York is almost the highest in the United States. The gallery owner has to pay for lights, heat, rent, taxes, printing invitations, pay to mail things, paying for advertising (commercials) and also has to pay the people who work in the gallery. Running a gallery is very expensive so they need 50% to pay to keep the business open.
14. Multiply the square feet by $5 for the answer.
15. 30 times the number of students. Divide that by 60 for the number of minutes.
16. 12 x 15 inches. Take each number and multiply by 1.5 for the answers.

Perspective

Vocabulary:

— Perspective (Per-spec-tiv)

— Horizon (Ho-rie-zon)

— Vanishing Point (Va-nish-ing)

— Parallel (Pare-ra-lel)

— Converging (Kon-ver-jing)

— Vertical (Ver-ti-kul)

— Eye Level

This is 1 Point Perspective. Everything seems to be going to one point "A".

Perspective

Vocabulary:

— Perspective: The illusion of three dimensional space on a flat surface.
     (It is how flat pictures look 3-D)

— Horizon: Where the sky meets the land.

— Vanishing Point: The place where all lines going away from you look
     like they will meet each other. (They converge)

— Parallel: Lines that are side by side and never touch or meet.
     (Like rail road tracks.)

— Converging: To come together. Lines that meet each other.

— Vertical: Up and down lines.

— Eye Level: The level of your eyes. The horizon is always at your eye level.

Coloring Spheres

Please color these spheres like in the example.

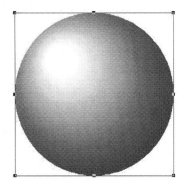

MONOCHROMATIC

Please color in the following 6 circles. See the sample so your circles look like shaded spheres too.

- Primary colors
- Secondary colors
- Analogous colors
- Complementary colors
- Any color plus black and white
- 1 color, use pressure to show light and dark.

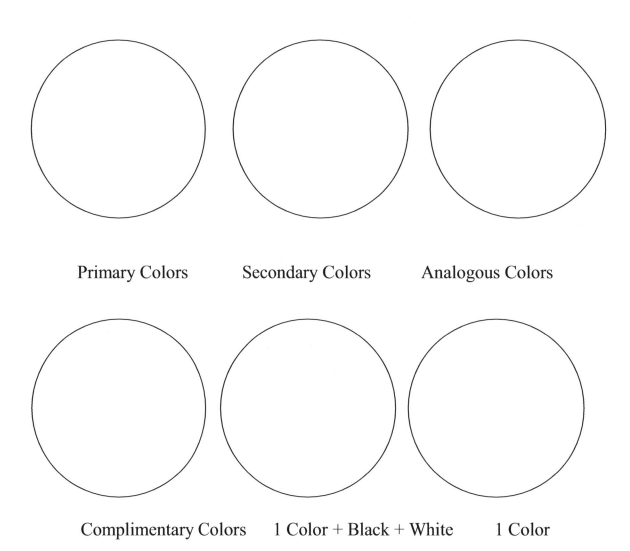

Primary Colors   Secondary Colors   Analogous Colors

Complimentary Colors   1 Color + Black + White   1 Color

4 Basic Forms

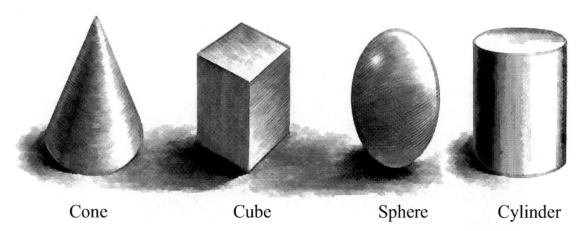

Cone   Cube   Sphere   Cylinder

Try drawing the 4 forms here. Color and shade them.

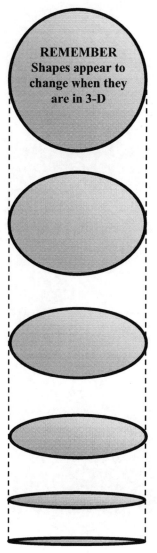

REMEMBER
Shapes appear to change when they are in 3-D

Face Proportions

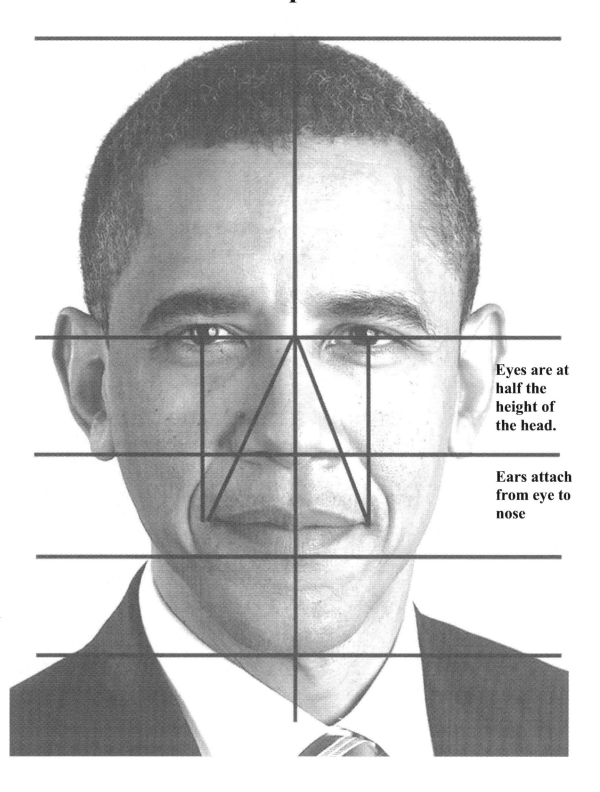

Eyes are at
half the
height of
the head.

Ears attach
from eye to
nose

Face Map Proportions

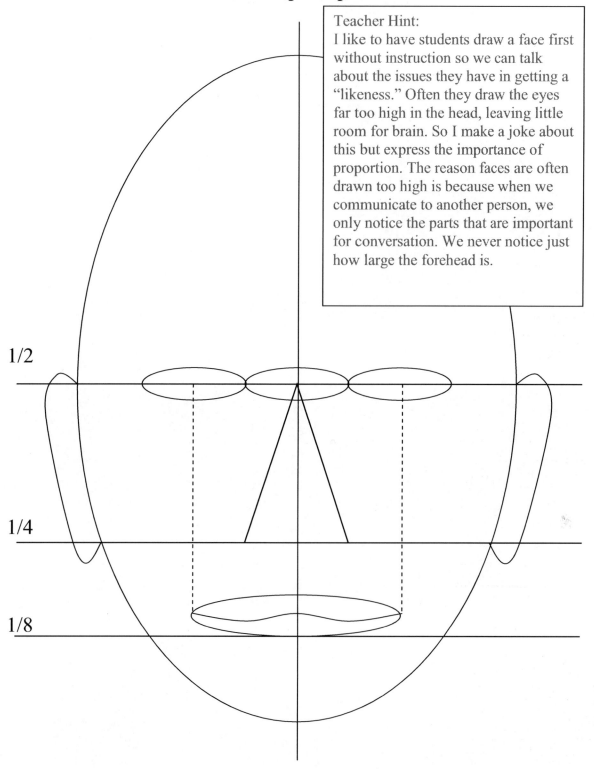

Teacher Hint:
I like to have students draw a face first without instruction so we can talk about the issues they have in getting a "likeness." Often they draw the eyes far too high in the head, leaving little room for brain. So I make a joke about this but express the importance of proportion. The reason faces are often drawn too high is because when we communicate to another person, we only notice the parts that are important for conversation. We never notice just how large the forehead is.

1/2

1/4

1/8

Draw a face here in proportion:

A: Please take 2 or 3 minutes to write about the following quote.

What does this mean?

"Feet, what do I need you for when I have wings to fly?"
~Frida Kahlo

_____

_____

_____

B Please take 2 or 3 minutes to write about the following quote.

What does this mean?

"Paintin's not important. The important thing is keepin' busy."
~Grandma Moses

_____

_____

_____

C: Please take 2 or 3 minutes to write about the following quote.

What does this mean?

"Everything has its beauty but not everyone sees it."
~Confucius

_____

_____

_____

D: Please take 2 or 3 minutes to write about the following quote.

What does this mean?

"Life is the art of drawing without an eraser."
~John W. Gardner

_____

_____

_____

E: Please take 2 or 3 minutes to write about the following quote.

What does this mean?

"Colors are brighter when the mind is open."
~A. Alarcon

_____

_____

_____

F: Please take 2 or 3 minutes to write about the following quote.

What does this mean?

"Lying in bed would be a perfect ... if only I had a colored pencil long enough to draw on the ceiling." ~Gilbert K. Chesterton

_____

_____

_____

G: Please take 2 or 3 minutes to write about the following quote.

What does this mean?

"Art is a line around your thoughts."
~Gustav Klimt

_____

_____

_____

H: Please take 2 or 3 minutes to write about the following quote.

What does this mean?

"Not everybody trusts paintings but people believe photographs."
~Ansel Adams

_____

_____

_____

I: **Please take 2 or 3 minutes to write about the following quote.**

What does this mean?

"One should really use the camera as though tomorrow you'd be stricken blind."
~Dorothea Lange

_____

_____

_____

J **Please take 2 or 3 minutes to write about the following quote.**

What does this mean?

"Painting is easy when you don't know how, but very difficult when you do."
~Edgar Degas

_____

_____

_____

K: **Please take 2 or 3 minutes to write about the following quote.**

What does this mean?

"Every child is an artist. The problem is how to remain an artist once he grows up." ~Pablo Picasso

_____

_____

_____

L: Please take 2 or 3 minutes to write about the following quote.

What does this mean?

"A day without art is like a garden without flowers."
~Lori McNee

_____

_____

_____

M: Please take 2 or 3 minutes to write about the following quote.

What does this mean?

"Art washes away from the soul the dust of everyday life."
~Pablo Picasso

_____

_____

_____

N: Please take 2 or 3 minutes to write about the following quote.

What does this mean?

"Art is like singing, some do it better than others,
but everyone can and should be doing it for their soul." ~Barbara Mason

_____

_____

_____

O: Please take 2 or 3 minutes to write about the following quote.

What does this mean?

"A man paints with his brains and not with his hands."
~Michelangelo

_____

_____

_____

P: Please take 2 or 3 minutes to write about the following quote.

What does this mean?

"Surely nothing has to listen to so many stupid remarks
as a painting in a museum." ~Edmond & Jules de Goncourt

_____

_____

_____

Q: Please take 2 or 3 minutes to write about the following quote.

What does this mean?

"Art without heart is craft."
~Eric Gibbons

_____

_____

_____

R: **Please take 2 or 3 minutes to write about the following quote.**

What does this mean?

"Imagination is more important than knowledge."
~Albert Einstein

_____

_____

_____

S: **Please take 2 or 3 minutes to write about the following quote.**

What does this mean?

"Only the artists and children see life as it is."
~Hugo von Hofmannstahl

_____

_____

_____

T: **Please take 2 or 3 minutes to write about the following quote.**

What does this mean?

"Create like a god, command like a king, work like a slave."
~Constantin Brancusi

_____

_____

_____

U: Please take 2 or 3 minutes to write about the following quote.

What does this mean?

"As a painter, I will never amount to anything important.
I am absolutely sure of it." ~Vincent van Gogh

_____

_____

_____

V: Please take 2 or 3 minutes to write about the following quote.

What does this mean?

"To be an artist you have to give up everything,
 including the desire to be a good artist." ~Jasper Johns

_____

_____

_____

W: Please take 2 or 3 minutes to write about the following quote.

What does this mean?

"He who works with his hands and his head and his heart is an artist."
~St. Francis of Assisi

_____

_____

_____

X: **Please take 2 or 3 minutes to write about the following quote.**

What does this mean?

"The EARTH without ART is just EH….."
~Unknown

_____

_____

_____

Y: **Please take 2 or 3 minutes to write about the following quote.**

What does this mean?

"I want to paint with colors that rhyme."
~Dave Watland

_____

_____

_____

Z: **Please take 2 or 3 minutes to write about the following quote.**

What does this mean?

"Painting is easy, getting it right is the hard bit."
~Danny Byrne

_____

_____

_____

Schools of Art - History

A "School Of Art" is another way to say a group of art or a style of art. We put things in groups all the time. We can put people in groups too like girls and boys. Religions are kinds of groups like Christians, Muslims, Jews, and Buddhists… Even your pets are put in groups like poodles, bull dogs, spaniels, and beagles…

We group these things by the way they look. Poodles all have curly hair, Dalmatians have black spots, Beagles are smaller and have brown spots.

Art is the same way. If you see a painting, with people wearing rich clothes like from a Cinderella Movie, and the trees look very fluffy, and the people look like they are rich and playing around, then it might be from the Rococo (Row-co-co) school of art.

If you see a painting of something you might see in a TV commercial, and it has very bright colors, it might be from the Pop Art school of art.

Rococo and Pop Art are schools of art. We will learn about 13 important ones. You should know there are hundreds of schools of art, but you will learn about just a few important ones. They are:

Renaissance (Re-na-sance)
Baroque (Ba-roke)
Rococo (Row-co-co)
Neo-Classical (Neo-Clas-si-kul)
Romanticism (Ro-man-ti-si-zum)
Realism (real-is-um)
Impressionism (Imm-pre-shon-is-um)
Cubism (Qb-is-um) or (Cube-is-um)
Dada (Da-da)
Surrealism (Sur-real-is-um)
Expressionism (X-pre-shun-is-um)
Abstract Expressionism (Ab-stract, X-pre-shun-is-um)
Pop Art

Research:

Pick one school of art from the previous page. Maybe your teacher will have you pick from a hat, so not everyone does the same thing. Write it here:

_____

Use the internet or the library to answer these questions:

1. What is the year that your school of art began? _____*
(* this may not be exact, but get as close as you can)

2. Name three artists of your school of art and their birth year

_____ born in _____

_____ born in _____

_____ born in _____

3. Many artists start after they are 20 years old. If you add 20 to their birth year, is your answer to number 1 still correct? Do you need to change it?

4. Name three famous artworks (painting, drawing, or sculpture) and the artist.

_____ made by _____

_____ made by _____

_____ made by _____

5. What must art from your school of art need to look like to be from that style?

_____

_____

_____

_____

POSTERS:

Working with a small group of two to four people, you are to create a poster that will teach others about that school of art.

Who is in your group? (Put your name in too)

_____,

_____,

_____,

_____,

RULES: You must include:
— Title (That's the school of art)
— General dates of the school of art
— ART from that period IN COLOR (You may photocopy and color in)
— Label all artwork

Written information should include:
— Written history of that school of art
— 4 or more artists working in that period
— Each artist must be shown with an artwork on the poster
— CLUES: If you saw a painting, how would you know it was from your "School Of Art" List some clues to know how to know the art's school

BONUS: Extra Credit
— Include an interesting fact like –Van Gogh went crazy because he held his brushes in his mouth and got slowly poisoned by his paint!
— QUOTE: Include a famous quote from artist in your school of art.

There is a sample poster on the next page and a sketch page after that.

Schools of Art Poster Project Sample by Students

Poster planning sketch page. School of art _____

Famous Artists for Research

If your teacher assigns a research paper, this is a list of artists that may be helpful. There are many thousands of artists, but this is a short list of some famous ones.

Pablo Picasso

Marcel Duchamp

Henri Matisse

Vincent Van Gogh

Claude Monet

Édouard Manet

Georgia O'Keeffe

Piet Mondrian

Paul Klee

Roy Lichtenstein

Claes Oldenburg

Christo and Jeanne-Claude

Michelangelo

Salvador Dali

Jackson Pollack

Mark Rothko

Paul Cezanne

Jasper Johns

Andy Warhol

Ansel Adams

Wayne Thiebaud

Georges Seurat

Rauschenberg

Albers Joseph

Grant Wood

Andrew Wyeth

Pierre Renoir

Chuck Close

M. C. Escher

Mary Cassatt

Alexander Calder

Rembrandt Van Rijn

Red Grooms

Dorothea Lang

Edvard Munch

Duane Hanson

Louise Nevelson

Raphael

Frank Stella

Romare Bearden

Frida Kahlo

Katsushika Hokusai

Edward Hopper

Jacob Lawrence

Henri Rousseau

Marc Chagall

Augustus Rodin

Norman Rockwell

George Segal

Artist Research Paper

Work copied from the internet or plagiarized will be a zero and referred to the office for disciplinary action. Use the Internet or library to find information, just… PUT IT IN YOUR OWN WORDS. Read, understand and then write.

Pick an artist from the list or find another one in an art book.

You must write a one page paper about an artist and their work plus include a photo and cover page.

Your paper must have:
— The name of the artist
— Birth and death dates of the artist and what country they are from
— "School of art" (This is the name of the style of their art, like Surrealism, Impressionism etc.)
— Basic history (a simple life story)
— Talk about his/her work and what is it that makes it special
— Write about one work of their art, answer why it is important or special.
— Include a copy, photocopy, print-out of the painting you are writing about on a separate page. Label it with name of the artists, and name of the art!
— On cover page, write where you found your information. (**Bibliography**)

Paper Rules:
— 1 full page.
— 1 inch borders/margins all the way around
— 14 pt font (Simple font like this one "Times New Roman" is good)
— SINGLE SPACED with NO spaces between paragraphs. (See the sample)
— Cover page with your name and additional information. (See the sample)

ALL WORK IS CHECKED FOR COPYING! Don't copy work!

DUE DATE _____, _____ points off for every day late.

A SAMPLE PAPER IS ON THE NEXT 3 PAGES

Your Name
Period

Artist's Name
Birth/Death Dates
School of Art

Bibliography

Book Title, Author, ISBN number
Or full web address
http://www.artcyclopedia.com/artists/hassenflaffa.html

Arthur Framanmatt was born in 1892 in New York City and died in 2001 in his beloved Antarctica. He was a surrealistic painter who was fascinated by painting fruit pits and animal hair, which he included in every painting.

Although born in New York he was raised on the top of Mount Fuji by his adopted Egyptian family; famous fur traders from Mexico. His mother specialized in selling seas shells by the sea shore, while his father was well known for his "Peter Piper" brand pickled peppers. Arthur loved drawing rubber baby buggy bumpers at a nearby factory. He was often seen by the factory custodian while drawing and became his student, soon covering the walls of the factory with murals of all kinds. This is when he began to paint peach pits with a few apple seeds into his paintings of giant wooly mammoths covered in French braids.

Framanmatt attended Burlington County Community College in his 80's, getting an advanced degree in fine art. He was commissioned by the college to create more murals, these became, what are known today as, the Fuzz Murals. Though fully recognized for their genius today, at the time of their installation, they were hated.

Later the artist completed a series in the same style, though miniature, for the Bordentown Street Fair. The works were a great hit and one sold to a major New York gallery owner. This gallery brought Mr. Framanmatt to Manhattan, holding several successful exhibitions where his "Fur and Seed" paintings would sell for several thousand dollars each.

Arthur experimented with many other subjects including gum wads, pastry crumbs, kitten dandruff, and the modestly successful series based on his photographs of belly-button fuzz. His works can be found in most major collections of art including the Museum of Modern Art of New York, Los Angeles, Paris, Baghdad, Fiji and the Bikini Islands.

Arthur is one of a small group of artists in the Dada School of art who created an offshoot called "Da-Dee" art. It is known for use of natural elements and the addition of odor to their works of art. Other Famous artists of this group were Pablo Dyapar, Samual Steekey, Michael Farfrumfartin, and Jennifer Deodorante', famous for her actual lack of smell, and her paintings of toenail clippings and gum wrappers.

The attached work is called *White Polar Bear in a Snowstorm* where the artist uses his lesser-known technique of white on white on white. All the elements of the painting are shown through the subtle use of texture, but the show was not popular, and nobody liked his work.

His great disappointment led to a deep depression and he moved to Antarctica and eventual died there in 2001. Recent video images do conclude that he was viciously attacked and killed by a pack of wild rabid penguins.

Though Arthur Framanmat is dead, his legacy lives on in museums around the world, though much of his work remains hidden in the vaults of museums.

White Polar Bear in a Snowstorm, by Arthur Framanmat, 1999

Before you hand in your report, use your check list:

Report Check List

Put an "**X**" in the box for the things you have done. Like this [**X**]

[__] The name of the artist

[__] Birth and death dates of the artist and what country they are from

[__] "School of art" (This is the name of the style of their art, like Surrealism, Impressionism, etc.)

[__] Basic history (a simple life story)

[__] Talk about his/her work and what is it that makes it special

[__] Write about one work of their art, answer why it is important or special.

[__] Include a copy, photocopy, print-out of the painting you are writing about on a separate page. Label it with name of the artists, and name of the art!

[__] On cover page, write where you found your information. (**Bibliography**)

[__] Is your name on the report?

Check that you have done these things with an "**X**" like this [**X**]

[__] 1 full page or more.

[__] 1 inch borders/margins all the way around

[__] 14 pt font (Simple font like this one "Times New Roman" is good)

[__] SINGLE SPACED with NO spaces between paragraphs. (See the sample)

[__] Cover page with your name and additional information. (See the sample)

Schools Of Art - Introduction

Let's find out more about the schools of art. Using textbooks, the internet, or library; try to complete as much of this information as you can.

1. Renaissance: Dates:_____

Definition:

What is special or unique about this school of art?

Two Artists: _____ & _____

2. Baroque: Dates: _____

Definition:

What is special or unique about this school of art?

Two Artists: _____ & _____

3. Rococo: Dates: _____

Definition:

What is special or unique about this school of art?

Two Artists: _____ & _____

4. Neo-Classical: Dates: _____

Definition:

What is special or unique about this school of art?

Two Artists: _____ & _____

5. Romanticism: Dates: _____

Definition:

What is special or unique about this school of art?

Two Artists: _____ & _____

6. Realism : Dates _____

Definition:

What is special or unique about this school of art?

Two Artists: _____ & _____

7. Impressionism : Dates _____

Definition:

What is special or unique about this school of art?

Two Artists: _____ & _____

8. Expressionism: Dates _____

Definition:

What is special or unique about this school of art?

Two Artists: _____ & _____

9. Cubism: Date _____ (*This one is an exact year*)

Definition:

What is special or unique about this school of art?

Two Artists: _____ & _____

10. Dada: Dates _____

Definition:

What is special or unique about this school of art?

Two Artists: _____ & _____

11. Surrealism: Dates _____

Definition:

What is special or unique about this school of art?

Two Artists: _____ & _____

12. Abstract Expressionism: Dates _____

Definition:

What is special or unique about this school of art?

Two Artists: _____ & _____

13. Pop art: Dates _____

Definition:

What is special or unique about this school of art?

Two Artists: _____ & _____

14. What style seems the most interesting and why?

_____

_____

_____

15. What painting did you see that you liked the most and why?

_____

_____

_____

Schools of Art Overview
Write 3 facts about each.

Renaissance

1. _____
2. _____
3. _____

Baroque

1. _____
2. _____
3. _____

Rococo

1. _____
2. _____
3. _____

Neo-Classical

1. _____
2. _____
3. _____

Romanticism

1. _____
2. _____
3. _____

Impressionism

1. _____
2. _____
3. _____

Realism

1. _____
2. _____
3. _____

Cubism

1. _____
2. _____
3. _____

Dada

1. _____
2. _____
3. _____

Surrealism

1. _____
2. _____
3. _____

Expressionism

1. _____
2. _____
3. _____

Abstract Expressionism

1. _____
2. _____
3. _____

Pop Art

1. _____
2. _____
3. _____

Schools of Art List

Renaissance – French word for "rebirth," This work showed Greek, Roman, or Bible stories, they tried to make the work look 3-D with perspective. It is the oldest style on this page, and looks old, from about the 1400s to the 1600s. Some artists would include Leonardo da Vinci, Michelangelo, (and the other Ninja Turtles ;-)

Baroque – Looks like it might be on stage and have a spotlight. Look for drama in the action or the lighting. Often has very dark and very light areas, but not always. You might see Musketeer's style clothes of the 1600s.

Rococo – Sickeningly Sweet, everything is rosy and RICH, it shows people playing. Cute, fluffy, and maybe naughty. Rococo is like Baroque but topped off with a tub of sugar. Look for Cinderella style dresses. (Mid 1700s)

Neo-Classical –The Neo-Classical were very political and HATED the Rococo arts as "empty headed." The paintings are VERY organized, serious, often with big shapes hidden in the paintings. These paintings often included Greek and Roman images so be careful to not confuse it with Renaissance. Most buildings in Washington DC are examples of this style. (Late 1700s)

Romanticism – In the early 1800s, it usually showed man and nature but not always peaceful. Sometimes man is using nature—like hills or mountains to fight a war, or hunt to feed his family, but man is never hurting nature in this style, the opposite may be true and dramatic!

Realism –Is what it sounds like. Realism showed the good and the bad. It began before there were cameras, so the artists tried to paint as much detail as they could. Before this time, people were usually painted prettier than they really were. (Mid 1800s)

Impressionism – Started in France in the 1860s, the artists tried to paint to show how important light is. Monet, Cassatt, Van Gogh, Cézanne, and Pissarro are Impressionist painters. These paintings are usually THICK with paint. Paintings are made while looking at what you are painting. Many of these paintings have a "Z" pattern hiding inside them.

Cubism – Started by Pablo Picasso with his painting in 1907 of Demoiselles d'Avignon. Usually the art looks shattered, and broken into shapes like broken glass, but you can still see what's going on.
NOT ALL work with shapes is CUBISM!

Expressionism – These paintings must have images you can understand but it is a little weird, or very strange to express emotions. The artists of this school of art use color or shape to help make the emotions stand out. Edvard Munch is an artist of this style. (Began near the 1920s)

Abstract Expressionism – NO pictures can be seen. The work looks like splashes, or layers of color, or child-like. *If you can't tell at all what's going on in the painting it is probably this style.* Began in New York in the 1940s

Dada – A strange art movement that started in Germany in the early 1920s. The artists tried to make fun of art and museum art. They would make things that most people thought was junk, or not "real" art, like a toilet up-side-down. Marcel DuChamp is a famous artist of this style.

Surrealism – Started in the 1920s and was often about dreams or the secrets in your brain. Art in the Surrealist style often looked dreamlike or impossible. Some artists were De Chirico, Salvador Dali, Rene Magritte, and Joan Míro.

Pop Art – Started in New York in the 1950s and 60s, a style of art that comes from **pop**ular culture including stuff you buy in a store (like soup or soda), commercials, simple every-day stuff, and cartoons. Some famous artists Keith Haring, Claes Oldenburg, and Andy Warhol.

Important art to remember

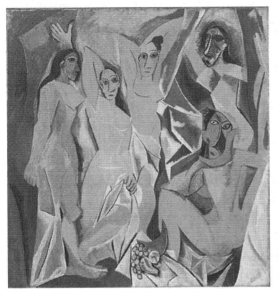

Pablo Picasso, **1907** of *Demoiselles d'Avignon*.

The painting above is the first painting in human history that a person was painted in a way that was different on purpose. They style is called Cubism, it was the first one! **Below** is the *Mona Lisa*, by Leonardo Da Vinci, a Renaissance Artist from the late 1400s. It is the most famous painting in the world!

The painting to the right →
…is a painting of a dream. The stuff in the painting is not real, but it is painted to look very real. This is called surrealism.

Starry Night, by Vincent VanGogh,

The painting above is special too, because the artist starts to use color to express his feelings. It is an Impressionist painting but some people call it post-impressionism.

Christina's World (above) by Andrew Wyeth is an example of Realism. It shows a lot of detail, and had both good things and bad things in the painting. People think it is a young girl, but it is really older lady named… Christina.

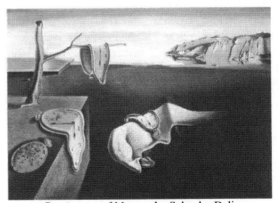

Persistence of Memory by Salvador Dali

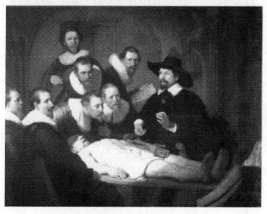

Schools of Art: Matching

Draw a line connect the art and the correct school of art.

Baroque: Looks like it might be on stage and have a spotlight. Look for drama in the action or the lighting. Often has very dark and very light areas, but not always. Musketeer's style clothes of the 1600's.

Neoclassical: The paintings are VERY organized, often with big shapes hidden in the paintings. These paintings often included Greek and Roman images so be careful to not confuse it with Renaissance.

Renaissance: This work showed Greek, Roman or Bible stories, they tried to make the work look 3-D with perspective. It is the oldest and looks old fashioned.

Rococo: Sickeningly Sweet, everything is rosy and RICH, it shows people playing. Cute and fluffy were their main ideas. Rococo is like Baroque but topped off with a tub of Sugar. Look for Cinderella style dresses.

Schools of Art: Matching

Draw a line connect the art and the correct school of art.

Dada: The artists tried to make fun of art and the people who liked museum art. They would make things that most people thought was junk, or not "real" art, like a toilet up-side-down.

Romanticism: Usually showed man and nature but not always peaceful. Sometimes man is using nature (like hills or mountains to fight a war, or hunt to feed his family, but man is never hurting nature in this work, but the opposite may be true.

Realism: Realism showed the good and the bad. It began before there were cameras, so the artists tried to paint as much detail as they could. Some of these paintings look like photographs.

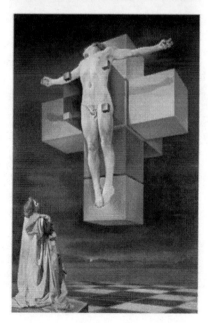

Schools of Art: Matching

Draw a line connect the art and the correct school of art.

Surrealism: Sometimes very real looking but somehow impossible or dream-like. Sometimes about the secrets in your brain.

Pop Art: A style of art that comes from popular culture including stuff you buy in a store, like soup or soda, commercials, simple every-day things, and cartoons.

Cubism: Usually the art looks shattered, and broken into shapes like broken glass, but you can still tell what's going on. **NOT ALL art with shapes is CUBISM!**

Schools of Art: Matching

Draw a line connect the art and the correct school of art.

Abstract Expressionism: NO pictures can be seen. The work looks like splashes, or layers of color, or child-like. If you can't tell at all what is going on in the painting, it is probably this style.

Expressionism: These paintings must have images you can understand but it is a little weird to express emotions. Though all art generally shows emotion, the artists of this school of art use color or shape to help make the emotions stand out.

Impressionism: The artists tried to show the way light changes the way things look. These paintings are usually THICK with paint. Paintings are made while looking at what you are painting. Many of these paintings have a "Z" pattern hiding inside them.

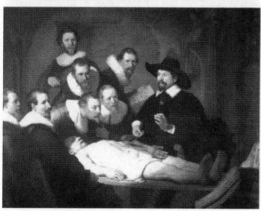

Schools of Art: Matching

Draw a line connect the art and the correct school of art.

Baroque: Looks like it might be on stage and have a spotlight. Look for drama in the action or the lighting. Often has very dark and very light areas, but not always. Musketeer's style clothes of the 1600's.

Neoclassical: The paintings are VERY organized, often with big shapes hidden in the paintings. These paintings often included Greek and Roman images so be careful to not confuse it with Renaissance.

Renaissance: This work showed Greek, Roman or Bible stories, they tried to make the work look 3-D with perspective. It is the oldest and looks old fashioned.

Rococo: Sickeningly Sweet, everything is rosy and RICH, it shows people playing. Cute and fluffy were their main ideas. Rococo is like Baroque but topped off with a tub of Sugar. Look for Cinderella style dresses.

Schools of Art: Matching

Draw a line connect the art and the correct school of art.

Dada: The artists tried to make fun of art and the people who liked museum art. They would make things that most people thought was junk, or not "real" art, like a toilet up-side-down.

Romanticism: Usually showed man and nature but not always peaceful. Sometimes man is using nature (like hills or mountains to fight a war, or hunt to feed his family, but man is never hurting nature in this work, but the opposite may be true.

Realism: Realism showed the good and the bad. It began before there were cameras, so the artists tried to paint as much detail as they could. Some of these paintings look like photographs.

Schools of Art: Matching

Draw a line connect the art and the correct school of art.

Surrealism: Sometimes very real looking but somehow impossible or dream-like. Sometimes about the secrets in your brain.

Pop Art: A style of art that comes from popular culture including stuff you buy in a store, like soup or soda, commercials, simple every-day things, and cartoons.

Cubism: Usually the art looks shattered, and broken into shapes like broken glass, but you can still tell what's going on. **NOT ALL art with shapes is CUBISM!**

Schools of Art: Matching

Draw a line connect the art and the correct school of art.

Abstract Expressionism: NO pictures can be seen. The work looks like splashes, or layers of color, or child-like. If you can't tell at all what is going on in the painting, it is probably this style.

Expressionism: These paintings must have images you can understand but it is a little weird to express emotions. Though all art generally shows emotion, the artists of this school of art use color or shape to help make the emotions stand out.

Impressionism: The artists tried to show the way light changes the way things look. These paintings are usually THICK with paint. Paintings are made while looking at what you are painting. Many of these paintings have a "Z" pattern hiding inside them.

*Teacher: Though strictly speaking Van Gogh was a **Post** Impressionist, I feel that on a pre-college level it is helpful to express him as an Impressionist as he displays the key qualities of Impressionism in an exaggerated way.*

What is abstract? (Ab-stract) means changed from what it really looks like. Some art is very abstract, some is just a little. Here are some pictures of President Obama that are abstracted.

Realistic Photo   Slightly Abstract   More Abstract   VERY Abstract

REMEMBER, if there is a subject, and the art is from a real thing, then it cannot be abstract expressionism. How about below? Is there a subject?

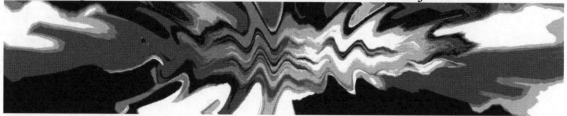

Your teacher will be able to show you many famous painting samples. Decide what school of art they belong to based on clues you see within the artwork.

Sketch Below: What school of art do you believe it to be from?

_____

What 3 pieces of evidence can you see?

1. _____

2. _____

3. _____

What was the real answer?

_____

If you were wrong, what did you miss?

What school of art do you believe it to be from?

Sketch Below:

_____

What 3 pieces of evidence can you see?

    1. _____

    2. _____

    3. _____

What was the real answer?

_____

If you were wrong, what did you miss?

Sketch Below:

What school of art do you believe it to be from?

_____

What 3 pieces of evidence can you see?

    1. _____

    2. _____

    3. _____

What was the real answer?

_____

If you were wrong, what did you miss?

Video Notes

Throughout the year, art videos will be played by the teacher or substitute. These will help with your art history information, or teach you how to do some art, or teach you something special about art. You will have to take some notes about what you see. This work is graded. You get a 100% if you participate and a zero if you do not. This will be very easy to do, but you must do some writing.

Writing one or two words is NOT enough. You must write a short sentence that tells us what you saw or what you heard. If the artist in the movie is painting a bird, you can write down, "The artist painted a bird." If the artist says, he was born in Mexico, you can write down, "The artist was born in Mexico." It is not hard but you need to pay attention.

We will try below. Your teacher will call out the first few facts to write down, then you need to try on your own. Spelling does not count, just try your best.

VIDEO NOTES – Sample

TITLE_____

Period___ Date __/__/__

Directions: Write 10 facts below based on the video WHILE YOU WATCH.
Two word facts, silliness, will not be acceptable. *This is GRADED.*

1. _____
2. _____
3. _____
4. _____
5. _____
6. _____
7. _____
8. _____
9. _____
10. _____

Double check that all facts have MORE than 2 words.

GRADED BY TEACHER: FULL CREDIT 100%   OR _____% Credit

Some Art Videos on Youtube.com
This was a working list in the Spring of 2010.

http://www.youtube.com/watch?v=ub6GTjY031Y	Food Art
http://www.youtube.com/watch?v=1qdYJmiLV2Q	Hand Turkey
http://www.youtube.com/watch?v=s7GYGmEcQJA	Hand Art
http://www.youtube.com/watch?v=JjUMvnsE4zo	More Hand Art
http://www.youtube.com/watch?v=2itCiI-ykYg	Hand Shadows
http://www.youtube.com/watch?v=hibyAJOSW8U	Fake Face
http://www.youtube.com/watch?v=orjALWsyaR4	Burger Painting
http://www.youtube.com/watch?v=HVhVClFMg6Y	Kinetic Sculpture, BMW Spheres
http://www.youtube.com/watch?v=WcR7U2tuNoY	Theo Jansen
http://www.youtube.com/watch?v=b694exl_oZo	Theo Jansen
http://www.youtube.com/watch?v=PH6xCT2aTSo	Inflatable Bag Monsters
http://www.youtube.com/watch?v=fZvoqNiOnG4	Coffee Art
http://youtube.com/watch?v=rV5NLOL7Fjk	"Sand Dancer"
http://youtube.com/watch?v=Gw933kKz7w8	23 Scraps of Paper
http://youtube.com/watch?v=EkUbYBo5xgs	Banksy in the Museum
http://youtube.com/watch?v=SIf3dfqIVg8	Lobo Skank Onesong
http://youtube.com/watch?v=JwsBBIIXT0E	Reverse Graffiti
http://www.youtube.com/watch?v=zl6hNj1uOkY	Doll Face
http://www.youtube.com/watch?v=i1wfWPtjxMA	Dirt Painting
http://www.youtube.com/watch?v=ONqgaVU_XPk	Cube Animation
http://www.youtube.com/watch?v=vPIpvFtZ4-k	Makeup Artists
http://www.youtube.com/user/notblu?blend=1	Blu Art, Animated Drawings
http://www.youtube.com/watch?v=awKJQ-HfEHc	Shepard Fairey (Obama Hope Poster)
http://www.youtube.com/watch?v=iXT2E9Ccc8A	Salvador Dali
http://www.youtube.com/watch?v=lRai9x8aD3A	Bansky London Show
http://www.youtube.com/watch?v=3SNYtd0Ayt0	Street Mural
http://www.youtube.com/watch?v=f4zoQSNX1Ys	Electronic Garden
http://www.youtube.com/watch?v=NZsqd-OgKhE	Vogal Art Collection
http://www.youtube.com/watch?v=BDlLh0jcJVY	60 minutes: Is this art?
http://www.youtube.com/watch?v=0CFPg1m_Umg	Spraypaint Art
http://www.youtube.com/watch?v=ghqoqz3yvts	Spraypaint Art
http://www.youtube.com/watch?v=eftdfXNICbY	Paper Towers
http://www.youtube.com/watch?v=3Un20p1NGuw	Black Hole - Office
http://www.youtube.com/watch?v=NmxX2r-uD8I	Thief?
http://www.youtube.com/watch?v=OjTOs1L3SBg	InSide, Short Film
http://www.youtube.com/watch?v=ZxmvRDTELy8	Sliding House
http://www.youtube.com/watch?v=4HMm9jrgDzM	Artistic 1-10 in Japanese Theme
http://www.youtube.com/watch?v=d2Y5mUJiaZI	Duchamp's Fountain
http://www.youtube.com/watch?v=QrtCcXXNcGA	Coin Making
http://www.youtube.com/watch?v=BM-JpePRWB8	Coin Manufacture
http://www.youtube.com/watch?v=10gStfTPBfg	Relief Sculpture
http://www.youtube.com/watch?v=HdXNWH06mPc	Tourist Trap Animation
http://www.youtube.com/watch?v=pLAma-lrJRM	Twitch Art

YOUTUBE Video Notes   DATE_____

Just write the title of the video and a short sentence about what you saw. 1 per video. As always, 1 and 2 word statements do not count.

1. _____ | _____
2. _____ | _____
3. _____ | _____
4. _____ | _____
5. _____ | _____
6. _____ | _____
7. _____ | _____
8. _____ | _____
9. _____ | _____
10. _____ | _____

YOUTUBE Video Notes   DATE_____

Just write the title of the video and a short sentence about what you saw. 1 per video. As always, 1 and 2 word statements do not count.

1. _____ | _____
2. _____ | _____
3. _____ | _____
4. _____ | _____
5. _____ | _____
6. _____ | _____
7. _____ | _____
8. _____ | _____
9. _____ | _____
10. _____ | _____

VIDEO NOTES – GRADED

TITLE_____

Period___ Date __/__/__

Directions: Write 10 facts below based on the video WHILE YOU WATCH. **Two word facts, silliness, will not be acceptable.** *This is GRADED.*

1. _____
2. _____
3. _____
4. _____
5. _____
6. _____
7. _____
8. _____
9. _____
10. _____
11. _____
12. _____
13. _____
14. _____
15. _____
16. _____
17. _____
18. _____
19. _____
20. _____

Double check that all facts have MORE than 2 words.

GRADED BY TEACHER: FULL CREDIT 100%   OR _____% Credit

Critique with sample:

Critique of artwork is by _Vincent van Gogh_ Title/Description: _Starry Night_

From 1 (not evident) to 10 (Advanced evidence) rate the following aspects of the project:

Neatness = _8_ , Completeness = _9_ , Originality = _10_ , Following directions = _10*_

What art element is the strongest in this project? _Color seems to be the most strong art element_

Evidence: _The use of contrasting color, and bold saturated color makes it stand out_

What art principle is strongest in this project? _Many are, but movement stands out for me._

Evidence: _The sky seems to swirl, the hills are like churning waves, stars seem to twinkle,_

What is most successful about this project? _*Van Gogh set out to try and do a painting of a night sky from observation, so he met his goal. It is a very original idea._

Besides completeness, what could be improved upon in this project: _There are some small portions of the canvas showing between paint strokes. Coloring the canvas first may have hid this._

What can you say about the artist based on their artwork (Be positive): _I feel that the artist wants us to pay attention to the beauty around us, maybe we don't pay attention enough._

Critique of artwork is by _____ Title/Description: _____

From 1 (not evident) to 10 (Advanced evidence) rate the following aspects of the project:

Neatness = _____, Completeness = _____,   Originality = _____,   Following directions = _____

What art element is the strongest in this project? _____

Evidence: _____

What art principal is strongest in this project? _____

Evidence: _____

What is most successful about this project? _____

_____

Besides completeness, what could be improved upon in this project: _____

_____

What can you infer about the artist based on their artwork (Be positive): _____

_____

- -

Critique of artwork is by _____ Title/Description: _____

From 1 (not evident) to 10 (Advanced evidence) rate the following aspects of the project:

Neatness = _____, Completeness = _____,   Originality = _____,   Following directions = _____

What art element is the strongest in this project? _____

Evidence: _____

What art principal is strongest in this project? _____

Evidence: _____

What is most successful about this project? _____

_____

Besides completeness, what could be improved upon in this project: _____

_____

What can you infer about the artist based on their artwork (Be positive): _____

_____

What is Your Level of Participation?

based on Phillip Schlechty's "Levels of Engagement"

www.tinyurl.com/Lgxbwem

A: Engagement: [High Attention--High Commitment]
The artist takes the project seriously creating an artwork that has meaning and personal value. The artist works through challenging visual problems, learning at the highest levels.

B: Strategic Compliance: [High Attention--Low Commitment] The artwork has basic or little connection or value to the artist but does associate the artwork with a desired outcome--a good grade. The artist avoids difficult visual challenges if it does not affect their grade and will retain little of what has been learned.

C: Ritual Compliance: [Low Attention--Low Commitment]
The artist does just enough to look like their working and avoid confrontation by the instructor. Their emphasis is on doing just enough to pass and be left alone. Student learning will be superficial and without depth.

D: Avoidance: [No Attention--No Commitment]
The artist makes little-if any-attempt to create a work of art or follow directions, but does not disrupt activities of other artists or participate in non-project work. The artist does not fully participate, learning little or nothing from the artwork or process.

F: Rebellion: [Diverted Attention--No Commitment]
The artist refuses to work, acts in ways that disrupt others, or participates in non-art related activities they would rather do. (Texting, socializing) Artist creates poor work if any. They actively resist exploring creative and thoughtful artworks.

Benchmark 1   Name _____ Pd. _____

Understanding Art Elements: Do a drawing below of an object you can see in the room, be sure to include EACH art element in some way. It can be obvious or subtle. Write how you have used each art element on the bottom of this paper to show your understanding. (Drawing 20 points, 10 points for each written answer)

Line : _____

Shape: _____

Color: _____

Form: _____

Texture: _____

Space: _____

Light: _____

Mass: _____

Power Standard: 1.1: The Creative Process: All students will demonstrate an understanding of the elements and principles that govern the creation of works of visual art.

Element	0 Not Proficient	6 Approaches Proficient	8 Proficient	10 Advanced
Line	none	Some visual that approaches the concept without clear knowledge.	Basic image that demonstrates understanding of the concept. Simple outline.	Example that shows a more advanced concept of the element, like using line to create suggest form through crosshatching, complicated edges, texture.
Shape	none	Some visual that approaches the concept without clear knowledge.	Basic image that demonstrates understanding of the concept. Clear but elementary shapes like triangles, circles, and squares.	Example that shows a more advanced concept of the element. Non outlined shapes, complex shapes, shapes that suggest form, use of shape motif...
Color	none	Some visual that approaches the concept without clear knowledge. Use of ONLY primary colors.	Basic image that demonstrates understanding of the concept. Use of both primary and secondary colors only.	Example that shows a more advanced concept of the element, like the use of tertiary colors, color for texture, use of chromatic gray...
Texture	none	Some visual that approaches the concept without clear knowledge.	Basic image that demonstrates understanding of the concept. Showing simple single texture.	Example that shows a more advanced concept of the element, like multiple textures, textures through color, organic textures.
Form	none	Some visual that approaches the concept without clear knowledge.	Basic image that demonstrates understanding of the concept. Clear but elementary forms, basic shading to suggest form.	Example that shows a more advanced concept of the element. Shading that appears to vary in intensity and size, use of complex forms.
Mass	none	Some visual that approaches the concept without clear knowledge, flat looking work.	Basic image that demonstrates understanding of the concept. Some sense of mass through the use of form.	Example that shows a more advanced concept of the element, like textures alluding to mass, or a strong use of form and shading.
Space	none	Some visual that approaches the concept without clear knowledge.	Basic image that demonstrates understanding of the concept. Showing a basic use of space through form or shading.	Example that shows a more advanced concept of the element, like the use of positive and negative space, or shadows on the surface under the object.
	0 Points	10 points	20 points	30 points
DRAWING	None	Drawing present but unrecognizable, little if any use of the elements present.	Off topic – not something present in the room and drawn from observation, but may include elements	Drawn from observation and include elements

ALTERNATE RUBRIC (focus on drawing proficiency):

	Criteria				Points
	1-Not Proficient	**2- Approaching Proficient**	**3-Proficient**	**4- Advanced**	
Drawing: Elements of Design	The assessment was turned in, but showed little evidence of any understanding of the elements and principles of design. Student is not proficient.	The student did the assessment adequately, yet shows a lack of planning and little evidence that an overall composition was planned. Student is approaching proficiency.	The artwork shows that the student applied the principles of design while using one or more elements effectively. Student has proficient awareness of the elements of design.	Planned carefully, made sketches, and showed an advanced awareness of the elements and principles of design. Student has an advanced awareness of the elements of design.	——
Craftsmanship	The student showed below average craftsmanship, lack of pride in finished artwork. Artwork showed no evidence of effort and a lack of understanding.	The student showed average craftsmanship; adequate, but not as good as the student's previous abilities, a bit careless.	With a little more effort in finishing techniques, the artwork could be considered exceptional.	All aspects of the artwork were considered and patiently completed. The finished product is a result of careful meticulous planning. The craftsmanship is exceptional.	——
Time & Effort	Class time was not used wisely. Little or no effort went into the artwork.	Class time was not used wisely. Little time and effort went into the planning and design of the artwork.	Class time was used wisely. Some time and effort went into the planning and design of the artwork.	Class time was used wisely. Much time and effort went into the planning and design of the artwork.	——
Description of Elements of Design	Described some elements of design with poor skill. Description did not match the drawing. Description is not proficient.	Described some elements of design with approaching skill. Some description matched the drawing with approaching proficient skill.	Described most elements of design in full detail. Description matched the drawing with proficient skill.	Described each element of design in full detail. Description matched the drawing with advanced skill.	——
Requirements	More than one requirement was not met.	One requirement was not met completely.	All requirements are met.	All requirements are met and exceeded.	——
				Total---->	

Exemplars

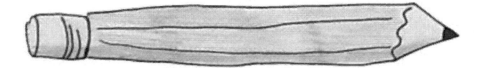

Line: I outlined my drawing of a pencil.
Shape: My lines create a rectangle and triangle.
Form: My shapes create a cylinder and cone
Color: I colored my pencil orange
Texture: I put little lines near the eraser to show ridges
Space: I added a shadow to show that it takes up 3-D space
Light: My shadow shows where the light cannot get to.
Mass: My light colors make the pencil also look light weight.

8 point sample answers

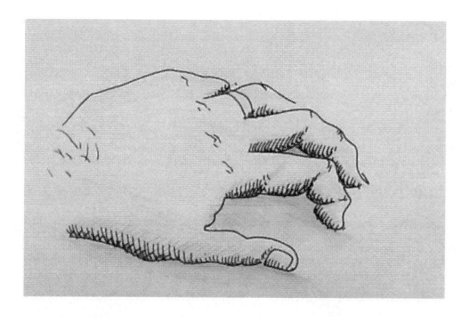

10 point sample answers

Line: I outlined my drawing with lines that show detailed contours
Shape: My lines create organic shapes of the hand.
Form: My shapes create organic forms, complex spheres and cylinders.
Color: I colored my hand with fleshtone, shaded with blue,
        and highlighted with yellow.
Texture: I used repeated lines to create different textures.
Space: I added a shadow to show that it takes up 3-D space and a
        cast shadow to suggest the negative space under the hand.
Light: I included shadows and highlights with both texture and color.
Mass: My light colors make the hand also look light weight, and
        the dark shadows suggest that they weight is on the underside.

Power Standard: 1.1: The Creative Process: All students will demonstrate an understanding of the elements and principles that govern the creation of works of visual art.

Directions: Using **only basic shapes**, visually describe four of the art principals visually and label them. The Art Principles are Balance, Movement, Emphasis, Pattern, Contrast, Variety, Unity.

0 points= off topic, 10 points = Approaches Understanding,   20 points = Understanding,
25 points = Advanced Understanding

Principal	0 Off Topic	10 Approaches Understanding	20 Understanding	25 Advanced Understanding
Balance	Off topic	Some visual that approaches the concept without clear knowledge.	Basic image that demonstrates understanding of the concept. Simple Symmetry.	Example that shows a more advanced concept of the principle, like asymmetrical Balance.
Variety	Off topic	Some visual that approaches the concept without clear knowledge. Might be mistaken for contrast.	Basic image that demonstrates understanding of the concept. Showing 3 or more different shapes.	Example that shows a more advanced concept of the principle, like showing it through placement, media, or by unexpected means.
Contrast	Off topic	Some visual that approaches the concept without clear knowledge.	Basic image that demonstrates understanding of the concept. Two opposite things illustrated	Example that shows a more advanced concept of the principle, like two opposite states of being.
Unity	Off topic	Some visual that approaches the concept without clear knowledge.	Basic image that demonstrates understanding of the concept. Showing simple similarity.	Example that shows a more advanced concept of the principle, like showing less obvious unity through proximity…
Emphasis	Off topic	Some visual that approaches the concept without clear knowledge.	Basic image that demonstrates understanding of the concept. Simple color or size difference.	Example that shows a more advanced concept of the principle, like showing other object leading to the point of emphasis.
Movement	Off topic	Some visual that approaches the concept without clear knowledge.	Basic image that demonstrates understanding of the concept. Simple object that normally moves.	Example that shows a more advanced concept of the principle, like showing movement through placement or leading the eye of the viewer.
Pattern	Off topic	Some visual that approaches the concept without clear knowledge.	Basic image that demonstrates understanding of the concept. Simple repetition of shape.	Example that shows a more advanced concept of the principle, like an organic pattern or conceptual repetition.

Art 1 Benchmark #3

NAME_____ Period ___

DIRECTIONS:

- **Using only primary colors, fill in this color wheel.**
- Put a "P" next to PRIMARY colors
- "S" next to secondary colors
- "W" next to warm colors
- "C" next to cool colors.
- "T" next to tertiary colors

Scoring: Each portion is 3 points.
_____ x 3 = _____ % correct

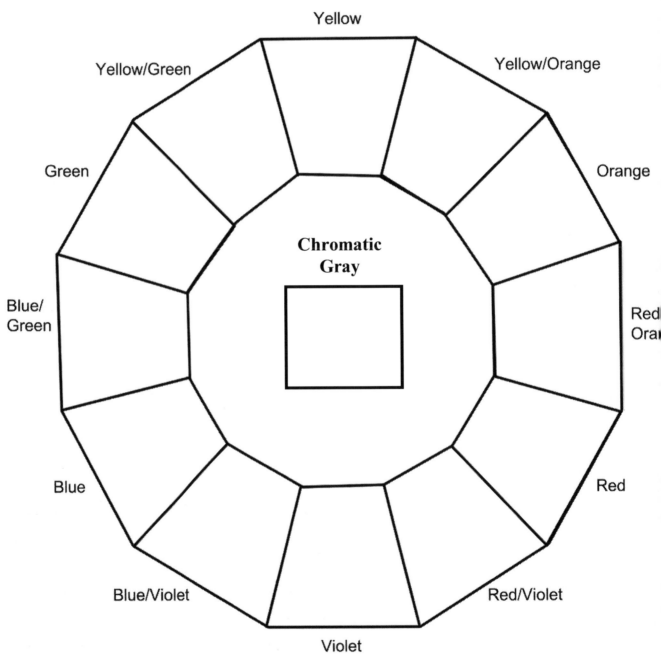

CCCS: 1.3.P.D.2 Create two and three-dimensional works of art while exploring color.

Art Elements

Draw an object from observation below and color it in using only primary colors and mixing those colors to make other hues. Your finished drawing must include the art elements of Line, Shape, Color, and Texture. On the next page explain how you used these elements. Be as specific as possible.

Try to show your "advanced" understanding.

Power Standard: 1.1: The Creative Process: All students will demonstrate an understanding of the elements and principles that govern the creation of works of visual art.

Explain your use of the art elements:

Line: _____

_____

Shape: _____

_____

Color: _____

_____

Texture: _____

_____

Scoring Rubric

Element	0 Not Included	10 Approaches Understanding	20 Understanding	25 Advanced Understanding
Line	none	Some visual that approaches the concept without clear knowledge.	Basic image that demonstrates understanding of the concept. Simple outline.	Example that shows a more advanced concept of the element, like using line to create suggest form through crosshatching, complicated edges, texture.
Shape	none	Some visual that approaches the concept without clear knowledge.	Basic image that demonstrates understanding of the concept. Clear but elementary shapes like triangles, circles, and squares.	Example that shows a more advanced concept of the element. Non outlined shapes, complex shapes, shapes that suggest form, use of shape motif...
Color	none	Some visual that approaches the concept without clear knowledge. Use of ONLY primary colors.	Basic image that demonstrates understanding of the concept. Use of both primary and secondary colors only.	Example that shows a more advanced concept of the element, like the use of tertiary colors, color for texture, use of chromatic gray...
Texture	none	Some visual that approaches the concept without clear knowledge.	Basic image that demonstrates understanding of the concept. Showing simple single texture.	Example that shows a more advanced concept of the element, like multiple textures, textures through color, organic textures.

Assessment: Graded by both the teacher and the student. Only the teacher's grade counts, but if there is a larger difference between the assessments, they can be discussed.

Project Title _____ Date Complete _____

Short Description _____

Assess a grade of "A, B, C, D or F." You may add + or – if you feel the need.

Student Assessment Below   **Teacher Assessment Below.**

Neatness _____   Neatness _____
Completeness _____   Completeness _____
Originality _____   Originality _____

Following Directions _____   Following Directions _____
Meeting Project Goals _____   Meeting Project Goals _____   _____
                                                                              Recorded Grade

----

Project Title _____ Date Complete _____

Short Description _____

Assess a grade of "A, B, C, D or F." You may add + or – if you feel the need.

Student Assessment Below   **Teacher Assessment Below.**

Neatness _____   Neatness _____
Completeness _____   Completeness _____
Originality _____   Originality _____

Following Directions _____   Following Directions _____
Meeting Project Goals _____   Meeting Project Goals _____   _____
                                                                              Recorded Grade

----

Project Title _____ Date Complete _____

Short Description _____

Assess a grade of "A, B, C, D or F." You may add + or – if you feel the need.

Student Assessment Below   **Teacher Assessment Below.**

Neatness _____   Neatness _____
Completeness _____   Completeness _____
Originality _____   Originality _____

Following Directions _____   Following Directions _____
Meeting Project Goals _____   Meeting Project Goals _____   _____
                                                                              Recorded Grade

----

Project Title _____ Date Complete _____

Short Description _____

Assess a grade of "A, B, C, D or F." You may add + or – if you feel the need.

Student Assessment Below   **Teacher Assessment Below.**

Neatness _____   Neatness _____
Completeness _____   Completeness _____
Originality _____   Originality _____

Following Directions _____   Following Directions _____
Meeting Project Goals _____   Meeting Project Goals _____   _____
                                                                              Recorded Grade

Universal Art Project Rubric

	Criteria				Points
	4 - A	3 - B	2 - C	1 - D	0 - F
Elements & Principles of Design	Planned carefully, made sketches, and showed an advanced awareness of the elements and principles of design. Student went above and beyond expectations	The artwork shows that the student applied the principles of design while using one or more elements effectively. Student met expectations.	The student did the assignment adequately, yet shows a lack of planning and little evidence that an overall composition was planned.	The assignment was turned in, but showed little evidence of any understanding of the elements and principles of art; No evidence of planning. Student did the minimum of work required.	_____
Craftsmanship & Neatness	All aspects of the artwork were considered and patiently completed. The finished product is a result of careful meticulous planning. The craftsmanship is outstanding. Project is pristine and well kept.	With a little more effort in finishing techniques, the artwork could be outstanding. Overall, the project is clean and without major defects like Folds/Rips	The student showed average craftsmanship; adequate, but not as good as the student's previous abilities, a bit careless. Minor folds or stray marks may be present.	The student showed below average craftsmanship, lack of pride in finished artwork. Artwork showed no evidence of effort and a lack of understanding. Includes obvious deficits like folds, rips, and/or stray marks.	_____
Time & Effort	Class time was used wisely. Much time and effort went into the planning and design of the artwork.	Class time was used wisely. Some time and effort went into the planning and design of the artwork.	Class time was not used wisely. Little time and effort went into the planning and design of the artwork.	Class time was not used wisely. Little or no effort went into the artwork.	_____
Execution, Originality, & Uniqueness	The artwork was successfully executed from concept to completion, with a novel and original approach.	The artwork was successfully executed from concept to completion. Unique & original with some evidence from samples.	The artwork was not successfully executed from concept to completion, with some unique aspects	The artwork was begun, but never completed. What work was done was highly derivative of the samples or other student's work.	_____
Requirements	All requirements are met and exceeded.	All requirements are met.	One requirement was not met completely.	More than one requirement was not met.	
				Grade ---->	_____

Testing Rules <<Block answers with this paper>>

#1, If you talk, look like you're talking, or communicate with anyone other than the teacher, YOU WILL RECEIVE A ZERO. NO Warnings, no chances, that's it. This includes "God Bless You" for sneezes. No Talking means NO TALKING.

#2. No Distractions like Tapping, rocking, Whistling, etc. DON'T DO IT.

#3. IF you have a question or need something clarified, RAISE YOUR HAND and wait for teacher. WHISPER your question and I will TRY to help.

#4. Work may be QUIETLY handed to the teacher when complete. You may take out something when EVERYONE at your table is done.

#5 IF YOU CHOOSE to write in your answers, you must write in the WORD.

Sample Artwork, *Starry Night* by Vincent Van Gogh

Directions: All the possible answers are in the box. Find the word that best fits in the blank spaces of the test and use the letter in front of the word for the **scantron** answer sheet. Some answers are used more than once, some are never used, some are there to trick you. (# = the answer is a number) If you write in the answers, please use the whole word.

A Red	A Tint	A Primary
B Orange	B Shade	B Secondary
A Yellow	C Value	C Chromatic gray
B Green	D Complimentary	D Equidistant
A Blue	E Analogous	E Saturation
B Purple	A Opposite	A 1
D Gray	B Triad	B 2
C Black	C Triangle	C 3
D White	D Neighboring	D 4
E Brown	E Warm	E **NO ANSWER**
A Hue	A. Cool	**Use in last spaces**

All colors come from basic colors more formally called (1)_____. There are (#2) _____ of these. They are (3) _____, (4) _____, (5)_____,(6) _____ These colors mix to make what are called the (7) _____ colors, of which there are _(#8) _____. These colors are (9) _____, (10) _____, (11) _____, (12) _____, (13) _____.

Orange and Blue mixed together will make a (14) _____ though it will look more like _(15) _____. These two colors also have a special relationship, because they are on _(16) _____ sides of the color wheel, they are called _(17) _____ colors. Red has a special relationship with Orange. Red and orange are both _(18) _____ colors and are also have a relationship called _(19) _____ colors, because they are _(20)_____ colors on the color wheel.

The basic colors have a special relationship too, they are _(21) _____ from each other on the color wheel and therefore are a _(22) _____. There is one more possible combination of colors that form this kind of relationship; they are called the _(23) _____ colors.

PRINCIPLES: Please answer the following by finding the **BEST** answer possible.

24. The area of focus or emphasis in Starry Night is the _____
    A. large Tree on the Left because it is so big and heavy.
    B. stars because they are so bright.
    C. swirl in the center because of its location, large size and dynamic shape.
    D. village with all its active geometric lines.
    E. bright moon because it is so bright.

25. Movement can be seen _____
    A. In the active Brush-strokes throughout the painting
    B. In the way the artist moves your eye in and out of the swirling sky.
    C. In the hills that seem to echo the movement of waves at the beach.
    D. In the sense of wind with the swirling sky lines and shapes.
    E. All of the above

26. Variety can be seen _____
    A. in the sky
    B. in the many different sizes of stars and points of light
    C. In the repetition of similar sized brushstrokes
    D. In the way the Moon is surrounded with lines
    E. None of the above

27. Unity is achieved by _____
    A. Everything being contained in a single scene.
    B. The Repetition of shapes throughout the painting
    C. The large tree anchoring the picture
    D. Putting Oranges and Blues in the same painting.
    E. All of the above

28. Balance is achieved by _____
    A. Asymmetrically balancing the large tree with the large bright moon.
    B. Symmetrically balancing the city.
    C. Putting the large mountain and the town on the left to create asymmetrical balance
    D. Brush strokes all over the surface of the painting.
    E. All of the above

29. Contrast is seen in _____
    A. The way everything seems to swirl in the image
    B. Bright colors opposing dark colors.
    C. The way the round stars are circled by rounded brush-strokes.
    D. In the very large tree in the front of the image
    E. The many types of stars we can observe.

30. Pattern can be seen in _____
    A. The all-over, organic repetition of yellow highlights.
    B. The Growing, wave-like repetitions of the hills in the background
    C. The way the artist applies paint to the canvas in short brushstrokes.
    D. All of the above
    E. Pick me because I want to get this answer wrong.

Art Elements Please answer the following by finding the **BEST** answer possible.

31. The art element of **Line** in Starry Night can be seen in the _____
    A. The way everything is painted in dashes.
    B. The heavy outlines around the buildings
    C. The outlines of the natural elements like hills, trees, and moon.
    D. All of the above
    E. None of the above

32. The art element of **Shape** in Starry Night can be seen in _____
    A. The dots that make up the stars.
    B. The lines around the buildings creating squares, rectangles, and triangles.
    C. The roughness of the paint's surface.
    D. The outlines of the tree and hills.
    E. The way the moon lights the scene.

33. The art element of **Form** in Starry Night can be seen in the _____
    A. in the way the moon could be viewed as a sphere.
    B. in the hills.
    C. in the tree
    D. in the way the dashed paint swirls around the canvas
    E. None of the above

34. The art element of **Color** in Starry Night can be seen in _____
    A. the use of cool analogous colors for most of the painting.
    B. the areas of the canvas that did not get painted.
    C. the space between the objects of the painting
    D. the night time theme
    E. None of the above

35. The art element of **Texture** in Starry Night can be seen in the _____
    A. smooth contours that make up the large tree.
    B. soft forms of the rolling hills that look like cool water.
    C. The hard edges of the buildings
    D. Brush strokes all over the surface of the painting.
    E. All of the above

36. The art element of **Mass** in Starry Night can be seen in the _____
    A. twinkling of the stars.
    B. shapes that outline the hills.
    C. the rounded brushstrokes that outline the stars.
    D. way that the heavy dark tree contrasts the light and bright moon.
    E. upward pointing church tower.

37. The art element of **Space** in Starry Night can be seen in the _____
    A. sky, because it's outer space
    B. yellows and blues
    C. use of foreground, middle-ground, and background, giving the painting a sense of depth.
    D. tree
    E. time it took the artists to actually make the work of art.

38. The art element of **Light** in Starry Night can be seen in the _____
    A. shadows that are suggested within the painting.
    B. use of blue and green that dominate the painting
    C. outlines of all the items within the painting
    D. cube-like forms of the city
    E. way the bright moon shines in the sky and the stars appear to twinkle

39. Please write the meaning of this quote on the back of your Scantron exam, or below, **in full sentence(s)**.

> *"A great fire burns within me, but no one stops to warm themselves at it,*
> *and passers-by only see a wisp of smoke"* ~Vincent van Gogh

_____

_____

_____

40. Please write how this quote applies to you **in a short paragraph**.

_____

_____

_____

_____

_____

_____

_____

_____

_____

_____

Test Answers:

Directions: All the possible answers are in the box. Find the word that best fits in the blank spaces of the test and use the letter in front of the word for the **scantron** answer sheet. Some answers are used more than once, some are never used, some are there to trick you. (# = the answer is a number)

A Red	A Tint	A Primary
B Orange	B Shade	B Secondary
A Yellow	C Value	C Chromatic gray
B Green	D Complimentary	D Equidistant
A Blue	E Analogous	E Saturation
B Purple	A Opposite	A 1
D Gray	B Triad	B 2
C Black	C Triangle	C 3
D White	D Neighboring	D 4
E Brown	E Warm	E **NO ANSWER**
A Hue	A. Cool	**Use in last spaces**

All colors come from basic colors more formally called (1)_**primary**_. There are (#2) _**3**_ of these. They are (3) __**red**__, (4) __**blue**__, (5)_**yellow**__,(6) __**E**__ These colors mix to make what are called the (7) _**secondary**_ colors, of which there are _(#8) _**3**_. These colors are (9) _**orange**_, (10) _**purple**_, (11) _**green**_, (12) _ **E** _, (13) __**E**__.

Orange and Blue mixed together will make a (14) _**chromatic gray**_ though it will look more like _(15) **brown**_. These two colors also have a special relationship, because they are on _(16) **opposite**_ sides of the color wheel, they are called _(17) _**complimentary**_ colors. Red has a special relationship with Orange. Red and orange are both _(18) **warm**_ colors and are also have a relationship called _(19) **analogous**_ colors, because they are _(20) **neighboring** _ colors on the color wheel.

The basic colors have a special relationship too, they are _(21) **equidistant**_ from each other on the color wheel and therefore are a _(22) **triad**_. There is one more possible combination of colors that form this kind of relationship; they are called the _(23) **secondary**__ colors.

112

PRINCIPLES: Please answer the following by finding the **BEST** answer possible.

24. The area of focus or emphasis in Starry Night is the _____
    A. Large Tree on the Left because it is so big and heavy.
    B. The stars because they are so bright.
    C. The Swirl in the center because of it's location, large size and dynamic shape.
    D. The Village with all it's active geometric lines.
    E. The Bright moon because it is so bright.

25. Movement can be seen _____
    A. In the active Brush-strokes throughout the painting
    B. In the way the artist moves your eye in and out of the swirling sky.
    C. In the hills that seem to echo the movement of waves at the beach.
    D. The sense of wind with the swirling sky lines and shapes.
    E. All of the above

26. Variety can be seen _____
    A. in the sky
    B. in the many different sizes of stars and points of light
    C. In the repetition of similar sized brushstrokes
    D. In the way the Moon is surrounded with lines
    E. None of the above

27. Unity is achieved by _____
    A. Everything being contained in a single scene.
    B. The Repetition of shapes throughout the painting
    C. The large tree anchoring the picture
    D. Putting Oranges and Blues in the same painting.
    E. All of the above

28. Balance is achieved by _____
    A. Asymmetrically balancing the large tree with the large bright moon.
    B. Symmetrically balancing the city.
    C. Putting the large mountain and the town on the left to create asymmetrical balance
    D. Brush strokes all over the surface of the painting.
    E. All of the above

29. Contrast is seen in _____
    A. The way everything seems to swirl in the image
    B. Bright colors opposing dark colors.
    C. The way the round stars are circled by rounded brush-strokes.
    D. In the very large tree in the front of the image
    E. The many types of stars we can observe.

30. Pattern can be seen in _____
    A. The all-over, organic repetition of yellow highlights.
    B. The Growing, wave-like repetitions of the hills in the background
    C. The way the artist applies paint to the canvas in short brushstrokes.
    D. All of the above
    E. Pick me because I want to get this answer wrong.

Art Elements Please answer the following by finding the **BEST** answer possible.

31. The art element of **Line** in Starry Night can be seen in the _____
    A. The way everything is painted in dashes.
    B. The heavy outlines around the buildings
    C. The outlines of the natural elements like hills, trees, and moon.
    D. All of the above
    E. None of the above

32. The art element of **Shape** in Starry Night can be seen in _____
    A. The dots that make up the stars.
    B. The lines around the buildings creating squares, rectangles, and triangles.
    C. The roughness of the paint's surface.
    D. The outlines of the tree and hills.
    E. The way the moon lights the scene.

33. The art element of **Form** in Starry Night can be seen in the _____
    A. in the way the moon could be viewed as a sphere.
    B. in the hills.
    C. in the tree
    D. in the way the dashed paint swirls around the canvas
    E. None of the above

34. The art element of **Color** in Starry Night can be seen in _____
    A. the use of cool analogous colors for most of the painting.
    B. the areas of the canvas that did not get painted.
    C. the space between the objects of the painting
    D. the night time theme
    E. None of the above

35. The art element of **Texture** in Starry Night can be seen in the _____
    A. smooth contours that make up the large tree.
    B. soft forms of the rolling hills that look like cool water.
    C. The hard edges of the buildings
    D. Brush strokes all over the surface of the painting.
    E. All of the above

36. The art element of **Mass** in Starry Night can be seen in the _____
    A. twinkling of the stars.
    B. shapes that outline the hills.
    C. the rounded brushstrokes that outline the stars.
    D. way that the heavy dark tree contrasts the light and bright moon.
    E. upward pointing church tower.

37. The art element of **Space** in Starry Night can be seen in the _____
    A. sky, because it's outer space
    B. yellows and blues
    C. use of foreground, middle-ground, and background, giving the painting a sense of depth.
    D. tree
    E. time it took the artists to actually make the work of art.

38. The art element of **Light** in Starry Night can be seen in the _____
    A. shadows that are suggested within the painting.
    B. use of blue and green that dominate the painting
    C. outlines of all the items within the painting
    D. cube-like forms of the city
    E. way the bright moon shines in the sky and the stars appear to twinkle

39. Please write the meaning of this quote on the back of your Scantron exam, or below, **in full sentence(s)**.

> *"A great fire burns within me, but no one stops to warm themselves at it,*
> *and passers-by only see a wisp of smoke"* ~Vincent van Gogh

_____

_____

_____

40. Please write how this quote applies to you **in a short paragraph**.

_____

_____

_____

_____

_____

_____

_____

_____

_____

115

TEST

Schools of art.

This is a scantron test. If you prefer to wire in your answers, you may do so.

Those completing the scantron version will probably have it graded before they leave today. Those who write in may not see their grade until the report card is sent home as it takes longer to grade those.

There is NO retake for this exam.
PLEASE follow normal testing rules:

1. **NO TALKING** for any reason, this included 'God bless You" for sneezes.
2. **NO NOISES** like tapping, rocking or kicking stuff. It is a distraction.
3. **IF** you have a question, please raise your hand and wait for teacher's help.
4. **COVER** your work. You risk a zero if you are cheating or helping someone cheat.
5. Hand in work when you are complete.
6. **REMAIN SILENT** until the last test is handed in or you risk a zero on your own test.

NAME: _____ **Period** _____

* Please put the following 5 schools of art in historical order from oldest to newest. **Use the letter in front of the word for your scantron.**

A. Dada, B. Renaissance, C. Pop Art, D. Impressionism, E. Neoclassical.

1. Oldest of the 5 would be _____
2. Next oldest _____
3. Next oldest _____
4. Next oldest _____
5. Newest of the 5 is _____

A. Renaissance	B. Baroque	C. Rococo	D. Neo-Classical	E. Romanticism
A. Realism	B. Impressionism	C. Cubism	D. Expressionism	E. Abstract Expressionism
A. Dada	B. Surrealism	C. Pop Art	D. Abstract	E. None of the above

* Please find the school of art **ABOVE** that has the following characteristics. **Use the letter in front of the word for your scantron.**

6. No Recognizable imagery _____
7. Dramatic Lighting _____
8. Having a shattered appearance _____
9. Dream-like imagery _____
10. Images from popular culture _____
11. Greek & Roman influence **Without** morality message. _____
12. Greek & Roman influence **With** morality message. _____
13. Thick use of paint, often outdoor scenes. _____
14. Paintings that look much like a photograph. _____
15. Sickeningly Sweet paintings of rich people. _____
16. Art that intentionally makes no sense. _____
17. Images of man and nature _____
18. Images with dramatic emotions shown through color and shape. _____

19. The first ever abstract work of art was painted by _____ called "Les Demoiselles d'Avignon"
    A. Warhol   B. DuChamp C. Picasso   D. DaVinci   E. Dali'

20. "Les Demoiselles d'Avignon" was created in what year? _____
    A. 1888 B. 1900 C. 1907 D. 1920 E. 1960

21. The most famous & most expensive painting in the world was created by _____
    A. Warhol   B. DuChamp C. Picasso   D. DaVinci   E. Dali'

Match the artist with their work of art. Use the letter in front of the mane on your scantron.
A. Picasso   B. Van Gogh   C. Andy Wyeth   D. Salvador Dali   E. Da Vinci

22. _____ (below)   23 _____ (below)

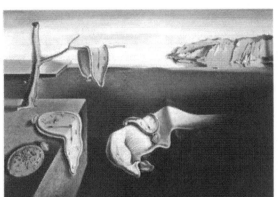

24. _____ (below)   25. _____ (below)

School of Art Identification:

Using the list below, identify what school of art each image belongs to. A helpful hint has been placed under each image. Take your time and think it through. If you are not sure, guess; you have a 20% chance of guessing right.

A. Renaissance	B. Baroque	C. Rococo	D. Neo-Classical	E. Romanticism
A. Realism	B. Impressionism	C. Cubism	D. Expressionism	E. Abstract Expressionism
A. Dada	B. Surrealism	C. Pop Art	D. Abstract	E. None of the above

26. Three boats being tossed by the sea in a storm
Man Struggles with Nature to survive

27. Five ladies painted in a geometric way.

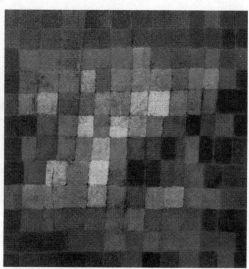

28. Wheel on a stool.

29. Multicolored squares, no subject.

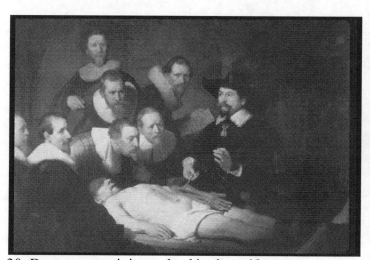

30. Doctors examining a dead body as if on stage

31. Sculpture of Jesus & Mary

32. Giant Spoon, 50 ft. tall, 100 ft long.

33. Rich people playing outside.

34. Man Screaming, Crazy Colors

35. Self portrait, looks like an advertisement.

36. Man returns home from hunting.

37. Brothers take an oath of honor and duty.

38. Detailed painting of a rabbit.

39. Thick paint in this image of a bedroom.

40. Castle on top of a floating rock.

Exam Answers

* Please put the following 5 schools of art in historical order from oldest to newest. **Use the letter in front of the word for your scantron.**

A. Dada,   B. Renaissance,   C. Pop Art,   D. Impressionism,   E. Neoclassical.

1. Oldest of the 5 would be   ___B__
2. Next oldest   ___E__
3. Next oldest   ___D__
4. Next oldest   ___A__
5. Newest of the 5 is   ___C__

A. Renaissance	B. Baroque	C. Rococo	D. Neo-Classical	E. Romanticism
A. Realism	B. Impressionism	C. Cubism	D. Expressionism	E. Abstract Expressionism
A. Dada	B. Surrealism	C. Pop Art	D. Abstract	E. None of the above

* Please find the school of art **ABOVE** that has the following characteristics. **Use the letter in front of the word for your scantron.**

6. No Recognizable imagery ____**Abstract Expressionism**_____
7. Dramatic Lighting ___**Baroque**_____
8. Having a shattered appearance __Cubism_____
9. Dream-like imagery _____Surrealism_____
10. Images from popular culture ___Pop Art_____
11. Greek & Roman influence **Without** morality message. ___**Renaissance**_____
12. Greek & Roman influence **With** morality message. ___**Neo-classical**____
13. Thick use of paint, often outdoor scenes. ___**Impressionism**_____
14. Paintings that look much like a photograph. ___**Realism**_____
15. Sickeningly Sweet paintings of rich people. __**Rococo**_____
16. Art that intentionally makes no sense. __**Dada**_____
17. Images of man and nature ___**Romanticism**_____
18. Images with dramatic emotions shown through color and shape. ___**Expressionism**____

19. The first ever abstract work of art was painted by _____ called "Les Demoiselles d'Avignon"
    A. Warhol   B. DuChamp   **C. Picasso**   D. DaVinci   E. Dali'

20. "Les Demoiselles d'Avignon" was created in what year? _____
    A. 1888 B. 1900 **C. 1907** D. 1920 E. 1960

21. The most famous & most expensive painting in the world was created by _____
    A. Warhol   B. DuChamp   C. Picasso   **D. DaVinci** E. Dali'

Match the artist with their work of art. Use the letter in front of the mane on your scantron.
A. Picasso   B. Van Gogh   C. Andy Wyeth   D. Salvador Dali   E. Da Vinci

22. _____C_____ (below)   23 _____D_____(below)

 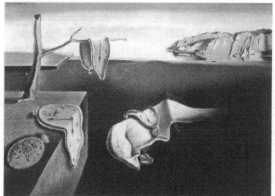

24. _____E_____ (below)   25. _____B_____(below)

School of Art Identification:

Using the list below, identify what school of art each image belongs to. A helpful hint has been placed under each image. Take your time and think it through. If you are not sure, guess; you have a 20% chance of guessing right.

A. Renaissance	B. Baroque	C. Rococo	D. Neo-Classical	E. Romanticism
A. Realism	B. Impressionism	C. Cubism	D. Expressionism	E. Abstract Expressionism
A. Dada	B. Surrealism	C. Pop Art	D. Abstract	E. None of the above

26. E. Romanticism

27. C. Cubism

28. A. Dada

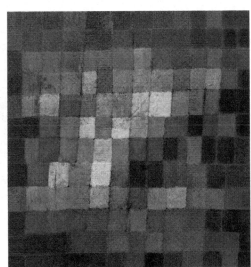

29. E. Abstract Expressionism

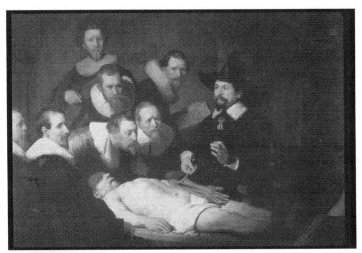

30. B. Baroque

31. A. Renaissance

32. C. Pop Art

33. C. Rococo

34. D. Expressionism

35. C. Pop Art

36. E. Romanticism

37. D. Neo-Classical

38. A. Realism

39. B. Impressionism

40. B. Surrealism

Interval Performance Based Assessments

Teacher:

The following pages are added as performance based evidence of learning, and are intended to be copied as double sided pages; drawing on the front, rubric on the back. Though they are set up for a portrait these could easily be done for a still life, drawing of the room, or nearly anything, though that same subject should be used each time. If you have a major project that you usually end your course with, portrait, perspective, etc., you may wish to have students use that as their subject in these assessments so at the end of the year, their final project acts as the final assessment in this series.

This assessment should be given on within the first week of class, end of the first quarter of learning, second quarter, third quarter, and the end of the course. It is possible to integrate this assessment into any formal "end of the quarter" assessment you may already give. Drawings should be of the same subject, so that as a whole, learning growth can be more easily seen through greater detail, use of tone, textures, proportion, expression, etc.

This need not be graded but can be an illuminating indicator of progress, and may be helpful should administration wish to see evidence of student learning from your students. It is also a nice package to give back to students at the end of the course to show progress. Should students continue taking more courses in art, it may be interesting to hold these examples, and review them annually.

I have removed the "grades" from the rubric, and altered its verbiage for this assessment. The rubric should be printed on the back of the assessment, so students do not focus on some kind of *judgment* of their work.

In the space below, draw your face, or the face of a neighboring student. Try to add as much detail as you can in the allotted time. This is not a graded assignment, we just need to see what skills you have before we formally begin this class.

Assessment Rubric

	Criteria				Points
	4	3	2	1	0
Elements & Principles of Design	Planned carefully, and showed an advanced awareness of the elements and principles of design. Student went above and beyond expectations	The artwork shows that the student applied the principles of design while using one or more elements effectively. Student met expectations.	The student did the assignment adequately, yet shows a lack of forethought and little evidence that an overall composition was planned.	The assignment was turned in, but showed little evidence of any understanding of the elements and principles of art; No evidence of planning. Student did the minimum of work required.	_____
Craftsmanship & Neatness	All aspects of the artwork were considered and patiently completed. The finished product is a result of careful meticulous planning. The craftsmanship is outstanding. Project is pristine and well kept.	With a little more effort in finishing techniques, the artwork could be outstanding. Overall, the project is clean and without major defects like Folds/Rips	The student showed average craftsmanship; adequate, but not as good as the student's previous abilities, a bit careless. Minor folds or stray marks may be present.	The student showed below average craftsmanship, lack of pride in finished artwork. Artwork showed no evidence of effort and a lack of understanding. Includes obvious deficits like folds, rips, and/or stray marks.	_____
Time & Effort	Class time was used wisely. Much time and effort went into the planning and design of the artwork.	Class time was used wisely. Some time and effort went into the planning and design of the artwork.	Class time was not used wisely. Little time and effort went into the planning and design of the artwork.	Class time was not used wisely. Little or no effort went into the artwork.	_____
Execution, Originality, & Uniqueness	The artwork was successfully executed from concept to completion, with a novel and original approach.	The artwork was successfully executed from concept to completion. Unique & original with some evidence from samples.	The artwork was not successfully executed from concept to completion, with some unique aspects	The artwork was begun, but never completed. What work was done was highly derivative of the samples or other student's work.	_____
Media Use	Media was used in novel ways. Strong evidence of experience.	Media was well used with some evidence of experience.	Basic use of media is evident.	Little evidence of media familiarity.	_____
				Total---->	_____

In the space below, draw your face, or the face of a neighboring student. Try to add as much detail as you can in the allotted time. This will be saved and compared to the last drawing you did.

Assessment Rubric

	Criteria				Points
	4	3	2	1	0
Elements & Principles of Design	Planned carefully, and showed an advanced awareness of the elements and principles of design. Student went above and beyond expectations	The artwork shows that the student applied the principles of design while using one or more elements effectively. Student met expectations.	The student did the assignment adequately, yet shows a lack of forethought and little evidence that an overall composition was planned.	The assignment was turned in, but showed little evidence of any understanding of the elements and principles of art; No evidence of planning. Student did the minimum of work required.	_____
Craftsmanship & Neatness	All aspects of the artwork were considered and patiently completed. The finished product is a result of careful meticulous planning. The craftsmanship is outstanding. Project is pristine and well kept.	With a little more effort in finishing techniques, the artwork could be outstanding. Overall, the project is clean and without major defects like Folds/Rips	The student showed average craftsmanship; adequate, but not as good as the student's previous abilities, a bit careless. Minor folds or stray marks may be present.	The student showed below average craftsmanship, lack of pride in finished artwork. Artwork showed no evidence of effort and a lack of understanding. Includes obvious deficits like folds, rips, and/or stray marks.	_____
Time & Effort	Class time was used wisely. Much time and effort went into the planning and design of the artwork.	Class time was used wisely. Some time and effort went into the planning and design of the artwork.	Class time was not used wisely. Little time and effort went into the planning and design of the artwork.	Class time was not used wisely. Little or no effort went into the artwork.	_____
Execution, Originality, & Uniqueness	The artwork was successfully executed from concept to completion, with a novel and original approach.	The artwork was successfully executed from concept to completion. Unique & original with some evidence from samples.	The artwork was not successfully executed from concept to completion, with some unique aspects	The artwork was begun, but never completed. What work was done was highly derivative of the samples or other student's work.	_____
Media Use	Media was used in novel ways. Strong evidence of experience.	Media was well used with some evidence of experience.	Basic use of media is evident.	Little evidence of media familiarity.	_____
				Total---->	_____

In the space below, draw your face, or the face of a neighboring student. Try to add as much detail as you can in the allotted time. This will be saved and compared to the last drawings that you did.

Assessment Rubric

	Criteria				Points
	4	**3**	**2**	**1**	**0**
Elements & Principles of Design	Planned carefully, and showed an advanced awareness of the elements and principles of design. Student went above and beyond expectations	The artwork shows that the student applied the principles of design while using one or more elements effectively. Student met expectations.	The student did the assignment adequately, yet shows a lack of forethought and little evidence that an overall composition was planned.	The assignment was turned in, but showed little evidence of any understanding of the elements and principles of art; No evidence of planning. Student did the minimum of work required.	_____
Craftsmanship & Neatness	All aspects of the artwork were considered and patiently completed. The finished product is a result of careful meticulous planning. The craftsmanship is outstanding. Project is pristine and well kept.	With a little more effort in finishing techniques, the artwork could be outstanding. Overall, the project is clean and without major defects like Folds/Rips	The student showed average craftsmanship; adequate, but not as good as the student's previous abilities, a bit careless. Minor folds or stray marks may be present.	The student showed below average craftsmanship, lack of pride in finished artwork. Artwork showed no evidence of effort and a lack of understanding. Includes obvious deficits like folds, rips, and/or stray marks.	_____
Time & Effort	Class time was used wisely. Much time and effort went into the planning and design of the artwork.	Class time was used wisely. Some time and effort went into the planning and design of the artwork.	Class time was not used wisely. Little time and effort went into the planning and design of the artwork.	Class time was not used wisely. Little or no effort went into the artwork.	_____
Execution, Originality, & Uniqueness	The artwork was successfully executed from concept to completion, with a novel and original approach.	The artwork was successfully executed from concept to completion. Unique & original with some evidence from samples.	The artwork was not successfully executed from concept to completion, with some unique aspects	The artwork was begun, but never completed. What work was done was highly derivative of the samples or other student's work.	_____
Media Use	Media was used in novel ways. Strong evidence of experience.	Media was well used with some evidence of experience.	Basic use of media is evident.	Little evidence of media familiarity.	_____
				Total---->	_____

In the space below, draw your face, or the face of a neighboring student. Try to add as much detail as you can in the allotted time. This will be saved and compared to the last drawings that you did.

Assessment Rubric

	Criteria				Points
	4	3	2	1	0
Elements & Principles of Design	Planned carefully, and showed an advanced awareness of the elements and principles of design. Student went above and beyond expectations	The artwork shows that the student applied the principles of design while using one or more elements effectively. Student met expectations.	The student did the assignment adequately, yet shows a lack of forethought and little evidence that an overall composition was planned.	The assignment was turned in, but showed little evidence of any understanding of the elements and principles of art; No evidence of planning. Student did the minimum of work required.	_____
Craftsmanship & Neatness	All aspects of the artwork were considered and patiently completed. The finished product is a result of careful meticulous planning. The craftsmanship is outstanding. Project is pristine and well kept.	With a little more effort in finishing techniques, the artwork could be outstanding. Overall, the project is clean and without major defects like Folds/Rips	The student showed average craftsmanship; adequate, but not as good as the student's previous abilities, a bit careless. Minor folds or stray marks may be present.	The student showed below average craftsmanship, lack of pride in finished artwork. Artwork showed no evidence of effort and a lack of understanding. Includes obvious deficits like folds, rips, and/or stray marks.	_____
Time & Effort	Class time was used wisely. Much time and effort went into the planning and design of the artwork.	Class time was used wisely. Some time and effort went into the planning and design of the artwork.	Class time was not used wisely. Little time and effort went into the planning and design of the artwork.	Class time was not used wisely. Little or no effort went into the artwork.	_____
Execution, Originality, & Uniqueness	The artwork was successfully executed from concept to completion, with a novel and original approach.	The artwork was successfully executed from concept to completion. Unique & original with some evidence from samples.	The artwork was not successfully executed from concept to completion, with some unique aspects	The artwork was begun, but never completed. What work was done was highly derivative of the samples or other student's work.	_____
Media Use	Media was used in novel ways. Strong evidence of experience.	Media was well used with some evidence of experience.	Basic use of media is evident.	Little evidence of media familiarity.	_____
				Total---->	_____

In the space below, draw your face, or the face of a neighboring student. Try to add as much detail as you can in the allotted time. This will be saved and compared to the last drawings that you did.

Assessment Rubric

	Criteria				Points
	4	3	2	1	0
Elements & Principles of Design	Planned carefully, and showed an advanced awareness of the elements and principles of design. Student went above and beyond expectations	The artwork shows that the student applied the principles of design while using one or more elements effectively. Student met expectations.	The student did the assignment adequately, yet shows a lack of forethought and little evidence that an overall composition was planned.	The assignment was turned in, but showed little evidence of any understanding of the elements and principles of art; No evidence of planning. Student did the minimum of work required.	_____
Craftsmanship & Neatness	All aspects of the artwork were considered and patiently completed. The finished product is a result of careful meticulous planning. The craftsmanship is outstanding. Project is pristine and well kept.	With a little more effort in finishing techniques, the artwork could be outstanding. Overall, the project is clean and without major defects like Folds/Rips	The student showed average craftsmanship; adequate, but not as good as the student's previous abilities, a bit careless. Minor folds or stray marks may be present.	The student showed below average craftsmanship, lack of pride in finished artwork. Artwork showed no evidence of effort and a lack of understanding. Includes obvious deficits like folds, rips, and/or stray marks.	_____
Time & Effort	Class time was used wisely. Much time and effort went into the planning and design of the artwork.	Class time was used wisely. Some time and effort went into the planning and design of the artwork.	Class time was not used wisely. Little time and effort went into the planning and design of the artwork.	Class time was not used wisely. Little or no effort went into the artwork.	_____
Execution, Originality, & Uniqueness	The artwork was successfully executed from concept to completion, with a novel and original approach.	The artwork was successfully executed from concept to completion. Unique & original with some evidence from samples.	The artwork was not successfully executed from concept to completion, with some unique aspects	The artwork was begun, but never completed. What work was done was highly derivative of the samples or other student's work.	_____
Media Use	Media was used in novel ways. Strong evidence of experience.	Media was well used with some evidence of experience.	Basic use of media is evident.	Little evidence of media familiarity.	_____
				Total---->	_____

Daily Exit Questions   Name: _____ Pd: _____ Week of: _____

Monday's Question: _____

_____

Artist's answer: _____

_____

Tuesday's Question: _____

_____

Artist's answer: _____

_____

Wednesday's Question: _____

_____

Artist's answer: _____

_____

Thursday's Question: _____

_____

Artist's answer: _____

_____

Friday's Question: _____

_____

Artist's answer: _____

_____

Exit Slip:
Name _____ Pd: _____
What can you do to improve your work?

Exit Slip:
Name _____ Pd: _____
What can you do to improve your work?

Exit Slip:
Name _____ Pd: _____
What can you do to improve your work?

Exit Slip:
Name _____ Pd: _____
What can you do to improve your work?

Exit Slip:
Name _____ Pd: _____
What can you do to improve your work?

Exit Slip:
Name _____ Pd: _____
What can you do to improve your work?

Exit Slip:
Name _____ Pd: _____
What can you do to improve your work?

Exit Slip:
Name _____ Pd: _____
What can you do to improve your work?

Exit Slip:

Name _____ **Pd:** _____

What do you still need more time to understand?

Exit Slip:

Name _____ **Pd:** _____

What do you still need more time to understand?

Exit Slip:

Name _____ **Pd:** _____

What do you still need more time to understand?

Exit Slip:

Name _____ **Pd:** _____

What do you still need more time to understand?

Exit Slip:

Name _____ **Pd:** _____

What do you still need more time to understand?

Exit Slip:

Name _____ **Pd:** _____

What do you still need more time to understand?

Exit Slip:

Name _____ **Pd:** _____

What do you still need more time to understand?

Exit Slip:

Name _____ **Pd:** _____

What do you still need more time to understand?

Exit Slip:

Name _____ **Pd:** _____

What is something new you learned today?

Exit Slip:

Name _____ **Pd:** _____

What is something new you learned today?

Exit Slip:

Name _____ **Pd:** _____

What is something new you learned today?

Exit Slip:

Name _____ **Pd:** _____

What is something new you learned today?

Exit Slip:

Name _____ **Pd:** _____

What is something new you learned today?

Exit Slip:

Name _____ **Pd:** _____

What is something new you learned today?

Exit Slip:

Name _____ **Pd:** _____

What is something new you learned today?

Exit Slip:

Name _____ **Pd:** _____

What is something new you learned today?

Exit Slip:

Name _____ **Pd:** _____

What connects you to your project?

Exit Slip:

Name _____ **Pd:** _____

What connects you to your project?

Exit Slip:

Name _____ **Pd:** _____

What connects you to your project?

Exit Slip:

Name _____ **Pd:** _____

What connects you to your project?

Exit Slip:

Name _____ **Pd:** _____

What connects you to your project?

Exit Slip:

Name _____ **Pd:** _____

What connects you to your project?

Exit Slip:

Name _____ **Pd:** _____

What connects you to your project?

Exit Slip:

Name _____ **Pd:** _____

What connects you to your project?

Exit Slip:

Name _____ Pd: _____

What do you *wish* you could do better on your project?

Exit Slip:

Name _____ Pd: _____

What do you *wish* you could do better on your project?

Exit Slip:

Name _____ Pd: _____

What do you *wish* you could do better on your project?

Exit Slip:

Name _____ Pd: _____

What do you *wish* you could do better on your project?

Exit Slip:

Name _____ Pd: _____

What do you *wish* you could do better on your project?

Exit Slip:

Name _____ Pd: _____

What do you *wish* you could do better on your project?

Exit Slip:

Name _____ Pd: _____

What do you *wish* you could do better on your project?

Exit Slip:

Name _____ Pd: _____

What do you *wish* you could do better on your project?

Exit Slip:

Name _____ **Pd:** _____

Response:

Exit Slip:

Name _____ **Pd:** _____

Response:

Exit Slip:

Name _____ **Pd:** _____

Response:

Exit Slip:

Name _____ **Pd:** _____

Response:

Exit Slip:

Name _____ **Pd:** _____

Response:

Exit Slip:

Name _____ **Pd:** _____

Response:

Exit Slip:

Name _____ **Pd:** _____

Response:

Exit Slip:

Name _____ **Pd:** _____

Response:

SKETCHBOOK IDEAS

Many of these may be turned into actual projects, but these sketchbook ideas are meant to be done in 1 class period or less as a way to warm up for larger projects. Consider posting this list and have students cross off the one they want to do when they finish project work too early. This way they stay meaningfully occupied.

Draw how you would symbolize the 4 seasons.

Design a metal of honor commemorating your greatest achievement in your life so far. If you do not have one you can think of, consider an accomplishment you hope to achieve in the future.

Re-imagine the wrapper for your favorite candy bar. Create a new design for it.

Fill a page with scribbles, and then look at them and reveal what can be seen in them. This is similar to looking at clouds and spotting objects in them, but here you color them in.

Rip a random small piece of paper from a magazine and draw it. Enlarge it to fill the page.

Draw the view through a window.

Write your name 30 times, in different sizes and directions, overlapping often to divide the page into many shapes. Color in using colors that express your mood today using the expressive colors and shapes worksheet.

Draw a tree from your imagination then draw a tree from observation. Which looks better to you? Why?

Trace your hand in an interesting position and turn it into an animal. DO NOT MAKE A TURKEY.

Find a common small object and enlarge it to fill your paper.

Draw yourself in a mirror but DO NOT look at the paper while you do it.

Draw a friend or family member with one continuous line. Do not lift the pencil until it is complete.

Find a tree and draw what is seen between the branches without drawing the tree itself.

Find a face in a magazine or photograph, turn it up-side-down and draw it up-side-down too.

Fill a page with shapes, get into every corner, but DO NOT lift your pencil until you are done. Color in using colors that express your personality using the expressive colors and shapes worksheet.

Draw an object that is reflective. Add a portion of your face into that reflection. (Cell phone, CD, compact, glass of water, spoon, Christmas ball...)

Draw some clouds from observation.

Draw your hand holding a CD. Draw as much of yourself in the mirror as you can see even if it is just a fragment.

Trace a leaf, trace the shadow it makes. Color in as realistically as you can like trompe l'oeil.

Trace your hand in an interesting position; fill it with patterns and color that express what you like to do with your hands.

Draw what you have in your pockets right now.

Draw a shoe, position the laces in such a way as to create a hidden face in your show. Draw it realistically but be sure to capture the idea of a face as well.

Take 2 unrelated objects and create a hybrid image of this new object. (Like scissors and a bird)

Spy on someone and draw them without them knowing.

Draw your meal or utensils.

Half fill a clear glass with water. Place 1 or 2 objects inside that are both in and out of the liquid (like a spoon or chopstick), draw it.

Take a common object that would relate to yourself, then repeat that object to make an animal that you also feel expresses your personality. Feel free to abstract and stretch the objects to make your animal.

Get a new pencil, do a drawing of something around you by holding the very end where the eraser is.

Write your name and a short statement in block letters, maybe a poem or memory, BUT do it with your eyes closed. Color in after you are done.

Using only color and shape, try to do a drawing that represents LOVE without using a heart.

Do a drawing of the feeling of WAR with colors and shapes and NO objects. Try other words.

Do a hybrid drawing of 2 unrelated animals as a new animal (lion & fish maybe). Be sure to have examples of both in front of you if possible.

Ask the closest person to you pick an object in the area, and then draw it.

Place a few objects on a white piece of paper, only draw the shadows.

Set an object in a box. Draw the object in the box; include the inside of the box in your drawing.

Draw an outline of a simple object.
- Draw the object again without lifting your pencil.
- Draw the object again without looking at your hand while you draw. Try to do it with a mostly continuous line.
- Draw the object's outline and shade with crosshatching lines.
- Draw the object again and use scribble lines to create shadow.
- Draw the object again only using dots for color and shadow.

Take a pattered fabric or shirt, drape it over a chair and draw it showing the pattern changes as the fabric folds and drapes.

Draw an object from observation above. Color the light side with warm colors (yellow through red) and the shaded side with cool colors like purple, blue, and green.

Put together a group of similarly colored objects. Set them up on a contrasting or opposite color for a still life drawing.

Draw a flag that would represent your family. Try to be symbolic. Use the worksheet in this book on the expressive qualities of shapes and colors.

Draw something from an unusual point of view.

Draw your hand drawing your hand in a funny way. (M.C. Escher did something like this)

Find a small simple, common object. Draw it large and turn it into an architectural design.

Draw your head realistically or as a cartoon. Add a large hole or opening to it and have objects escaping from that hole that tell a story about what goes on in your mind.

Draw your bedroom as if it was inside a container like a teapot, jar, cardboard box…

Draw what you imagine the inside of your stomach looks like after the last meal you ate.

Trace an object about the size of this page, onto a page. Turn it into a very different object by how you finish the drawing. A pair of scissors may become a bird. You may add onto the object as you wish, try not to erase much of the original outline.

Cover half of your face with an object, and then create a self portrait.

Draw an original super hero with a power you wish you had.

Draw a stabbed object. (Like a piece of fruit with a pencil stabbed into it) Make the drawing with exaggerated sense of emotion.

Draw someone talking. Fill the background with their words in a creative way. This could be a historical figure or someone around you today.

Draw something flying that would not normally be able to fly.

Write an expressive word in large fat bubble-letters. Fill in the letters with images that relate the meaning of the word.

Draw an animal based on a photograph of it, BUT only draw it with letters found in its name. It is okay to abstract the letters to make them fit. Use the colors of the animal to finish it.

Design an item of clothing, color and texture it.

Draw the kind of house you would like to live in.

Draw your hand pointed away from you toward an object, draw both your hand and the object. Overlap a bit if you can to add realism and a hint of perspective.

Use candles, burn sticks and draw a still life with home-made charcoal.

Draw a how-to label or poster for something you know how to do. If it is too complicated, illustrate just 1 to 4 steps of the process.

Draw a simple cartoon that illustrates the last time you were embarrassed.

Draw something with wings that normally would not have them.

Draw a wall with windows, and details of adjacent items like bookshelves, chairs, etc. Then draw an unexpected environment through the window.

Draw yours or a friend's face, divide it into 4 parts, and color each section with symbols for 4 things that are important to that person.

Trace your hand and draw what might be inside if you were an awesome robot.

Paste down half a face from a magazine. Choose an attractive model. Finish the other half of the face as if they were an alien.

If you could design your very own cell phone, what would it look like?

Draw a container, and on the back draw something unexpected that would be inside the container. Hold the page up to the light to see an x-ray view of both.

Design a piece of jewelry and use a symbol from your own cultural background in it.

Draw a piece of foil with a few wrinkles in it.

Place a coin under a page, rub a pencil over the page to create an embossed image. Then draw your hand holding the coin.

Draw a design you think would make a cool tattoo for you. Remember that tattoos are often symbolic of thing important to the person wearing it.

Draw the *thing* that lives under a child's bed.

Draw someone's ear from about 6 inches away from them. Be so close you can see every detail.

Using a flashlight, draw an object and its shades and highlights, but light it from an unusual point of view. (Like a face with the light below the chin, or still life lit from below.

Crumple a page, flatten it lightly so the creases are still obvious, then draw the page.

Draw a CD cover for your favorite song.

Remove your socks and shoes and draw your foot. How would you redesign a common road sign? Yield, Stop, No Running, Poison...

Draw yourself as if you were 100 years old.

Draw your home as a castle but include details that are there right now.

Crumple this page, lightly flatten it, and trace the wrinkles making what you can imagine into the creases. This is similar to finding objects in clouds. As you stare, object will become apparent.

Draw something dry as if it was wet.

Have a friend lay down on the floor. Draw their portrait while sitting above their head so their face is up-side-down. Your drawing will be up-side-down as well.

How would you re-design your hand to be better than it is? If you were into basketball, how might it be different? Consider your hobbies and activities.

What might a flower look like on an alien planet?

Design a new cologne bottle for either a great scent, or something very bad.

Willy Wonka remade an environment out of candy, what would you draw an environment out of?

Create a new label for your favorite beverage.

Pick a playing card and do a design based on that card that no linger looks like a playing card. Use repetition and pattern if it helps.

Create a cover for a ridiculous comic book.

Draw something in the room no one notices.

Lay on the floor and look up. Draw part of the room with this unusual perspective.

Put your leg up on the table and draw your leg, shoe and all, in perspective.

When you cross your eyes, you see double. Draw something around you as if you had double vision. Find a creative way to handle overlapped areas.

Do a portrait of a friend, but re-imagining their hair in a way that shows off their personality.

Create an advertisement for yourself as if you were a product in a store.

Create your initials in a very ornate and decorative way, like old illuminated manuscripts.

Draw the trophy you wish you could win.

Draw the first thing you would buy if you won the lottery.

Draw your hand holding your favorite possession.

Draw what it looks like sitting in the front of your car, and put something unexpected in the rear-view mirror.

Draw something pretty next to something ugly.

Draw a piece of popcorn to fill this page.

Draw something floating in a magical way.

Hold a tube of paper up to your eye and draw your point of view. (If you have glasses, maybe you can tape a small tube to them.)

Stand on something tall and draw your view looking down.

While lying on the floor, draw what you see from that perspective as if you were a bug.

Draw an object that makes noise. Draw what you imagine that noise might look like if it could be seen.

Sit in the back of a bus or car and draw your point of view. Feel free to change the scene through the window or make it realistic.

Draw something lit by a candle.

Draw two objects side by side that should never be put together.

Draw two objects side by side that represent opposite themes: War and peace, good and evil, love and hate…

Make a drawing that expresses a lie either literally, figuratively, or symbolically.

Draw an object as if it were in-side-out.

Draw the surface of a coin with a water droplet on it. If you have a magnifying glass, use it.

Draw a new and unique dinosaur.

Do a drawing of a person combined with an animal. The Egyptians did this a lot.

Draw a soft object with a steel skin with screws, rivets, and bolts.

Draw a cute animal as if it were Frankenstein's pet.

Draw an animal you consider unappealing, as cute.

Draw an object from observation but re-arrange its parts in an unexpected way.

Draw an advertisement for a product you would not like but make it seem appealing.

Draw two objects side by side but change their scale. For example, you might have a giant ant next to a tiny teacup.

Crumple a picture from a magazine and draw it as you see it.

Design a new kind of chair.

Do a line drawing of your shoe, and color it in the way you think would look interesting.

Life is often full of choices. Draw a portrait of yourself, divide the face in half, and show two potential life choices you will need to make as an adult in the design. (You as a teacher or you as a hairdresser) Use symbols and colors in the portrait to show the possible directions your life might take.

Take a common object and draw it as if it was a skeleton. What would the skeleton of a pear look like?

Design a monument for a common object, like a monument to a thumbtack.

Draw a face card from a deck of cards making you the queen, king, jack, or joker.

Draw what you see reflected in a bowl or plate of water. It will reflect better if the bowl is a dark color.

Draw your home or backyard from an aerial perspective. (From above)

Draw a mysterious doorway.

Imagine you ARE your favorite animal. Do a drawing you think that animal would draw if it could or from its point of view.

Draw an amazing sand castle on the beach.

The Tao of Teaching Art

1. Every project must be designed to incorporate the student's life or experience.
Instead of making a monster, my students might make a gargoyle that would protect them from a specific fear through their choices of symbols, forms, material, and colors. Instead of a color wheel, students can create a linear contour drawing of a personal still life, and color with color wheel concepts. Connect the project to the student experience and they will be invested in the outcome. With this method every project is unique, personal, and expressive.

2. Every project must have a tie-in to core courses.
When we grid—we teach geometry. When we make sculptures—we teach engineering. When we teach color mixing—physics. When we create illustrations for stories—we teach literature. When we review the styles of art from da Vinci to Warhol—we teach history. Ultimately, we teach creative problem solving and divergent thinking skills. Continue this tradition, and share with students that though this is art, it is also geometry, science, history, etc. Your students will succeed at higher levels in school, and you have a job you can defend against cuts.

3. Every student deserves a little one-on-one time.
Sit with students, one-on-one, to learn about their lives and motivations. Students are better motivated by people they feel care about them.

4. Keep it fun. It's art after all.
Avoid overly academic exercises and *crafy kitsch*. Do projects you would have liked to have done when you were a child. Silliness, exploration, imagination, and inventiveness help motivate and engage students.

5. Students should plan work with a sketch, a paragraph, or list, and organize ideas with clear parameters and expectations.
This avoids the use of materials you did not intend, waste, and creates a student-generated plan.

6. Flexibility; be ready to change ideas or methods with the tone of the class.
If students seem unmotivated, it may be an indication that you need to switch gears, re-motivate, or ask questions to understand student hesitation. It may also mean production steps were too large, a sample was too vague, or the project should be taught in smaller increments.

7. Love what you do, do what you love, and the students will follow you anywhere.
Children are emotional tuning forks. They can sense if you are *phoning it in*, faking it, or do not really care. Do projects that excite you; share your passion, yourself, and success will be assured.

8. Be dependable, predictable, and a good example.
Plan, prepare, and be consistent. Students do not have to *like you*, but they need to *respect* you. If your expectations are clear, and your classroom management is evenhanded, they will see you as fair. If you need to correct behavior, speak from the heart, and explain why change needs to happen. Corrections starting with "I" are better motivators than demands beginning with "You."

Our #1 Selling Resource For Art Teachers!

If you found this book helpful, Firehouse Publications has many more titles
specifically designed for the art teacher.

Please visit www.Firehouse Publications.com

Firehouse Publications can offer direct bulk discounts to schools.

Contact us through our website.

Made in the USA
San Bernardino, CA
14 February 2016